THE RMF JOB SEARCH WORKBOOK

How to Gain Access and Find a Position in the Hidden Job Market

Jim Clayton

ISBN: 0-7872-2080-9

Printed in the United States of America
10 9 8 7 6 5 4 3 2 1

Dedication

This work is dedicated to my wife, partner, editor and best friend, Michele.

CONTENTS

Acknowledgments

I'd like to thank Ray Castillo, Elaine Stover, Betty Barwegan, Dean Barnes, Chris Helms, and Carole Howard for editing and voicing their valuable opinions.

Chapter One

So, You're Looking For A Job!

There are many different motivations for initiating a job search. The most common reasons I hear (and I think I've heard them all) are:

- relocation to new geographic location
- first professional position after graduation from college
- inability to get along with a manager/supervisor/partner
- insufficient room for personal and professional growth
- untenable internal political situations
- ethical or philosophical incompatibility
- career unsuitability
- lay-offs
- disciplinary termination

Of all the potential reasons and justifications listed above notice that I've not included:

- it's more fun than working
- sheer joy and pleasure of conducting a job search

Job hunting is not considered, by most, a fun and leisure time activity. Even for those individuals who have done it often and are unusually suave and skilled, the thought of conducting a prolonged job search campaign causes anxiety!

When job hunting, common sense dictates that you should maximize every effort to find the best position as quickly, cost effectively, and efficiently as possible (get the most "bang for your buck," so to speak).

I've never understood why anyone would spend so much time and money developing cover letters and resumes but fail to invest those same limited resources to establish a job search plan which would ultimately lead to achieving the desired results.

This form of logic is akin to a carpenter deciding to build a house. The carpenter purchases the best available hammer and saw and begins construction, room by room, without a blueprint. As one room is completed, the next room is begun. At the end of construction, the carpenter has a house. However, since the house was built without a construction plan, the overall layout will be poor and the house will be different from what the carpenter really wanted.

Without a plan you might get lucky and find a position. If you are very lucky, it might even be the long-term career opportunity that you desire. However, retention statistics indicate that a high percentage of college graduates will leave their initial employer within three years. Many seem to settle for the first position offered because they fear there will be few other options.

In 1992, the Department of Labor approximated that 20% of all college graduates were working in non-college level jobs with 3% remaining unemployed. In 1995, approximately 1.2 million students will receive college degrees. If forecasts prove to be correct, the employment outlook for college grads through the year 2005 are slightly less favorable. (The American Workforce: 1992-2005, Bulletin 2452, April 1994, U.S. Department of Labor, Bureau of Labor Statistics)

If you are a recent graduate competing in today's highly competitive job market, it is possible that you will find your first professional position through on-campus interviewing. Some will, but many will not. You are even less likely to find your first position by blindly groping through the classified advertisements, professional periodicals, job fairs, employment agencies or job hotlines. Some will, but again, many will not!

What I've said might leave you feeling discouraged, angry, shocked or overwhelmed, but that is not my objective. The purpose of this workbook is not to frighten you. My hope is to enlighten you, urge you, and teach you how to accomplish three tasks:

- ❑ plan your job search
- ❑ develop job search goals
- ❑ apply a job search strategy that enables you to not only use published resources but also tap into the hidden job market

The hidden, or unadvertised, market, has long been a mystery to most job seekers. Approximately 70% of the total job market is hidden or unadvertised. Accessing these positions, along with those that are advertised, is a necessity for college graduates competing in today's marketplace.

The Research, Mail, Follow-up System, or RMF, is a tested and proven plan that will give you the power and knowledge to successfully compete in today's marketplace. Your workbook includes a detailed explanation of the RMF Job Search System with flow charts, 10 proven job search goals and 60 RMF Employer Contact Forms.

It's time to take control of your job search.

Let's get started!

Stop Blaming It All on Your Resume and Cover Letter

For over 19 years I have assisted employment seekers to develop job search campaigns and strategies that yield results.

In most cases it's fairly easy to determine the major causes for an ailing or a failing employment search. Many ask me to evaluate and revamp their resume and cover letter, feeling that these are the primary cause of their job hunting woes. They are usually wrong!

I am not trying to downplay the power and importance of strong marketing tools, for they are truly a necessity in an employment search. Recruiters receive hundreds of poorly written resumes and cover letters. Many are constructed as if they were autobiographies or historical documents rather than sales tools. Effective resumes and cover letters are designed to help the job seeker get a foot in the door. With a bit of research, most job seekers can build marketing materials that are substantial enough to do the job they are designed to do.

The greatest challenge facing your job search is not the content and design of your resume and cover letter, but how you apply these tools in the marketplace. Solely faulting a resume and cover letter for not getting the interviews you wish is comparable to blaming your automobile for carelessly crashing itself into a telephone pole as you sit complacently behind the steering wheel. If you think your resume and cover letter need help, see an advisor, do some research, or buy a book on the subject. After that, stop blaming your resume and start looking at how you are applying it!

Developing clear goals and planning an effective strategy to approach the job market are essential steps necessary for a successful employment search. Unfortunately most job seekers spend very little time planning and a great deal of time mailing resumes and hoping that someone will call them for an interview.

If no job search goals and strategies are established, none can be accomplished.

"People don't plan to fail, they fail to plan."
Unknown

From this day forth, you are responsible for the success of your job search. Luck is not a factor. Planning, hard work and persistence will lead to your goal.

Seven Ways Your Job Search Can Crash and Burn

Shotgunning, Snoozing, Paper Pushing, Expertising, Reckless Researching, Agency-Seeking, and HR Hypers!

Developing your strategy and getting off to a good start is one of the most difficult aspects of your job search. Although I hesitated opening the workbook on a negative note, I felt it was important to identify how your job search might go, or already has gone, awry. Following are seven examples of ineffective job search strategies commonly applied by job hunters today. These tactics almost always guarantee a marginally successful, if not totally failed, job search. If you fit into any of the categories discussed on the following pages, your job search is on a course to crash and burn.

Do these tactics sound like the ones you are using?

Shotgunning

Shotgunners are under the impression that a good job search involves sending one hundred or more cover letters and resumes in one afternoon. If you are a shotgunner, your cover letters are typically addressed, "To whom it may concern" because you have neither the time nor interest in conducting the proper research to determine how you might make a contribution to the firms to which you are applying. Shotgunners are convinced that high volume exposure to the job market is the key to finding a position. Most shotgunners don't keep track of where they apply. They feel that if the company is interested they will initiate the follow-up. Shotgunners believe that follow-up on the part of the applicant is an unnecessary bother and expense. Unfortunately, unless you are uniquely qualified and your timing is unnaturally perfect the company probably won't call you; they might not even send you a rejection letter! Without proper tracking and follow-up, shotgunners won't even know if the company received their resume.

Example of a shotgun that backfired:
In 1991, I met a student who sent over 150 resumes and "to whom it may concern" cover letters into the marketplace in one weekend (to a shotgunner volume equals results). He did not track his resumes and made no follow-up telephone calls. For his effort he received "three disappointing interviews and a handful of rejection letters." Shotgunning wastes your time and your money! Don't do it!

Snoozing

Snoozing, though not considered a job search tactic, is a common practice used by many who consider themselves to be job seekers. If you are a snoozer, you never really get your job search started. Instead of crashing and burning, you can't seem to get yours off the ground. Sure, you'll pick up the Sunday newspaper, but soon the focus of your attention is on the sports page instead of the employment ads. You've collected all the telephone numbers for the local job hotlines, but never call them. Snoozers lack a "sense of urgency" and the self-discipline necessary to move their job search from wishing and hoping to doing! Snoozers complain about how hard it is to find a job, but seldom engage in the necessary activities to find one. If you are a snoozer, remember this old employment agency saying, "When you snooze, you lose!"

Paper Pushing

Paper pushers almost exclusively use the printed media. If you're a paper pusher, you've contacted all of your friends, relatives, professors, neighbors, and business acquaintances and feel as though your job search network is tapped-out. When your network leads dried up, so did your subsequent endeavors to network and seek positions in the unadvertised job market. Now your job search is limited to the published market. Cover letters and resumes are addressed to the name or title placed in the ad. Unfortunately, your resume is almost assuredly on its way to the Human Resources Department—the place where job seekers find the highest degree of competition and highest probability of rejection. Although obtaining only marginal results, paper pushers happily send their resumes along with throngs of other paper pushers who exclusively use newspaper advertisements. As a sole source of employment leads, the printed media is not enough!

Read This

Always use the published job market as a job search source, for it would be frivolous and irresponsible to ignore it. Obviously, individuals do find employment through the classified ads or employers would stop using them. However, many recent graduates are disappointed and disillusioned as they try to find entry level positions through the newspapers. Don't let that frighten you. Keep looking there but, more importantly, learn to expand your search. To create a proper balance, direct about 30% of your job search to the published job market while focusing 70% into the unpublished or hidden job market.

Expertising

Definition of an expertiser: Someone who's afraid to take a chance and try something new because then he/she wouldn't be an expert anymore.

Expertisers are specialized paper pushers who only answer published advertisement that describe them to a "T." If the required skills, or qualifications, are even slightly out of line with the ones contained in their previous positions, or they feel that their grasp will be stretched slightly beyond their perceived reach, they do not apply.

If you are an expertiser, it is not unusual for you to feel that you are working very hard on your job search. In reality, you may have only sent a few resumes to potential employers over a three to six month period. As an expertiser, you spend a great deal of time seeking, but never quite finding the position you wish. Often you are puzzled when you see lesser qualified candidates getting job offers you want. You wonder, "How did they do it? I'm more qualified than they are."

Expertisers seem to be so engrossed by a fear of rejection, embarrassment, or failure that they refuse to take a reasonable risk which could lead to possible success and advancement. Take a chance, without a little risk there are few rewards.

Reckless Researching

Reckless researchers are blood relatives of expertisers. If you are a reckless researcher, you'll spend weeks researching an organization before even considering submitting a resume. With great precision and deliberation, you examine and study, and study and research, and then research some more.

The result of all your highly meticulous pre-interview research is one of two scenarios:

- ❑ your resume is not submitted
- ❑ it is not submitted in a timely enough manner to put you in contention for the position

My point is this: at some time you must actually make the plunge or nothing will happen.

Don't misunderstand what I am saying! Research is the foundation, and almost certainly, the principal difference between a successful and unsuccessful employment candidacy. Without it you can only expect a minimal level of achievement. However, you must send out your resume if you wish to find a job!

A resume does you no good sitting in your briefcase, unless you're carrying that briefcase to an interview!

To all reckless researchers:

WHEN IN DOUBT, SEND IT OUT!

Agency-Seeking

Agency-seekers place their employment search solely in the hands of others, usually search firms or employment agencies. If you are an agency seeker, your typical job search day consists of calling your headhunter or employment consultant once in the morning and once in the afternoon. You hope to hear about all the terrific new job leads that your agent has uncovered for you since yesterday. After a few weeks, you begin to wonder why your headhunter has stopped returning your phone calls and suddenly acts as though you're a carrier of the black plague when you eventually do hunt them down.

There is nothing wrong with working with these organizations, and they can be an asset to your search. I worked in the employment industry for 14 years and found that many of these firms have earned excellent reputations, are professionally managed, and exceptionally skilled at what they do. But generally speaking, an employment firm is only as good as the individual consultant with whom you are working. Also most employment firms tend to work with experienced individuals (that's why companies are willing to pay a fee for their services).

If you decide to work with an employment firm, select a consultant who is honest, easy to communicate with, knows your industry, and eagerly wants to work with you. If you don't like the service an employment firm is providing you, fire them and go elsewhere.

Be aware that if you are dealing with copious numbers of search firms at the same time, contact and fee conflicts may arise between those firms. This can have a negative effect on you. Over a period of 14 years, I saw it happen on a number of occasions. Also, be sure that your employment firm is not indiscriminately shotgunning your resume into the market place without doing proper research and follow-up.

HR Hypers

HR hypers are under the impression that a good job search begins and ends in the HR or Human Resources Department. If you are an HR hyper, you are certain that the HR Department is aware of all employment needs within each of the company's operational departments.

Why would anyone consider sending their resume anywhere else? You are sure that even though hundreds of others have also answered a newspaper advertisement, your resume will receive proper attention, get a thorough reading, and be properly directed by that recruiter or HR manager based on a comprehensive knowledge of the position. WRONG, WRONG, A THOUSAND TIMES WRONG!

If you are prospecting for positions, stay away from the Human Resources Department. At the very least do not make them your only contact.

In most situations, if the Human Resources Department has not been directed by management from an OPERATIONAL DEPARTMENT to seek candidates or given job specifications from which to recruit, the job seeker will receive a "your resume is under advisement" or an outright "rejection" letter.

Here are a few examples of operational departments

Accounting	Engineering
Finance	Customer Service
Sales	Marketing
Quality Control	Purchasing/Logistics Management
Manufacturing	Computer Information Systems

These are only a few. Research will enable you to determine the department and title of the individual who is the hiring authority for the position for which you are applying. Remember, you can always go back and apply through the Human Resources Department if you are unable to acquire the name and title of the hiring authority.

Why Should You Work with Hiring Authorities in Operational Departments?

Dealing with "Hiring Authorities" who manage "Operational Departments" presents you with:

- ❑ lesser degrees of competition from other candidates who have, along with hundreds of others, sent their resume to the HR Department
- ❑ access to an individual with an intimate knowledge of the positions, or potential positions, that may be opening in the near future
- ❑ the opportunity to make a direct contact at the place that the position is created, altered or completely redesigned
- ❑ greater access to network leads in the hidden job market if you are rejected

The demands placed on today's HR departments are immense. Not only are they responsible for recruiting, but their accountability has been extended to other areas which include training, employee relations, salary, benefits administration, and union negotiations, just to name a few. With all of these multiple and diverse responsibilities, it is very easy for your resume to be placed in the "resume grinder" with hundreds of others (be they solicited or unsolicited). The "resume grinder" is a cruel machine that allows only a few select resumes to be passed on to an individual able to make a hiring decision (a hiring manager within an operational department).

Stay Out of the Resume Grinder

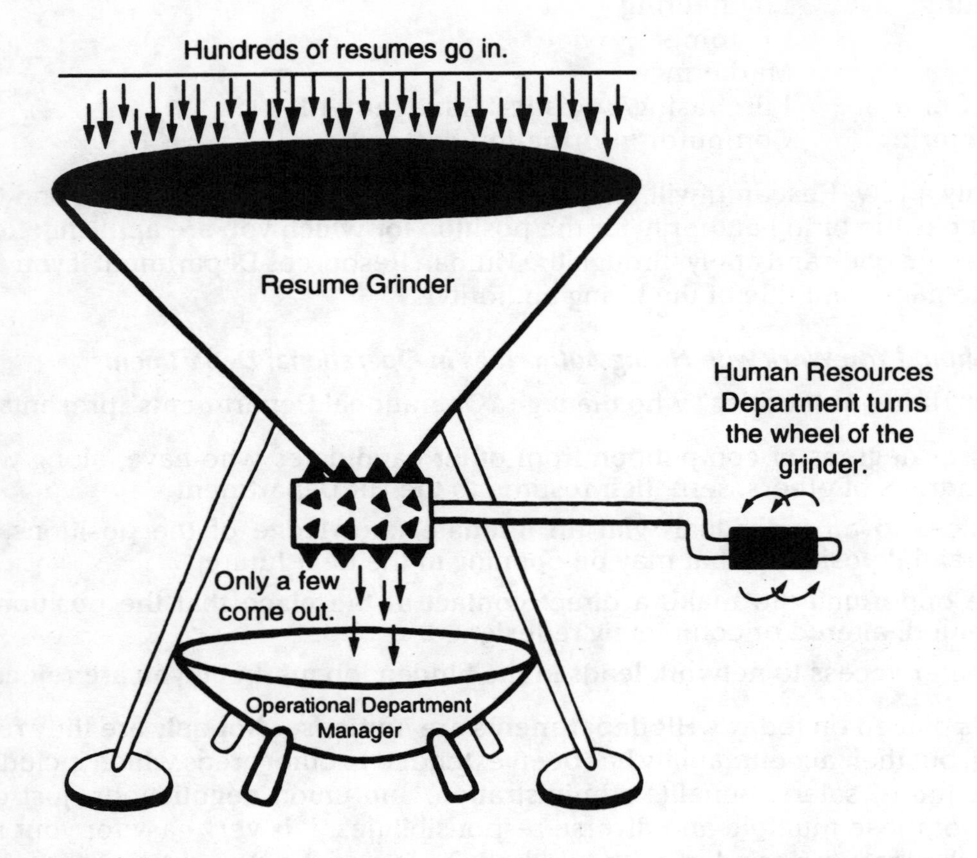

Most HR departments do their jobs very well; however, the job they do might not be in your greatest interest or benefit. Even for a highly qualified recruiter, who has knowledge of the jargon/key words of the position for which you are applying, it is easier to screen a resume than find reasons to qualify it. Candidates whose resumes do not make it past this lowest level of screening will not be placed in contention for the position and advance to a higher level of progressive evaluation.

As previously mentioned, most people feel that their job search woes are caused by their resume and cover letter. As you can see, there is a high probability that this is not the case.

If any of the previously defined approaches describe the way you have been attacking the job market, you've already identified the major source of your job search woes.

CHAPTER TWO

10 JOB SEARCH GOALS

Setting goals is an important part of your job search. Listed below are 10 Job Search Goals that you will use in the RMF system. By setting these goals at the beginning of your job search, you are establishing a sturdy foundation upon which it can be built. Read them, remember them, and refer back to them. You will be using them soon. If any of the terms mentioned below seem strangely new to you, don't be concerned; they will be defined and explained in Chapter 3.

1) Identify and apply to hiring authorities. Send your resume to Human Resources Departments only after you have exhausted all efforts to identify a hiring authority.

2) Research and send your resume and cover letter to 10 to 15 new companies every 10 to 15 days, especially if you are unemployed. This kind of "followed-up resume volume" is an important key in your job search.

3) Job search "down time" is unacceptable. While waiting for your resumes to get to the desk of the hiring authority, begin researching your next group of 10 to 15 organizations.

4) Make follow-up telephone calls on every resume you send. Take the initiative, don't expect employers to call you. If you don't plan to follow-up, don't send it. (That's how important follow-up is!)

5) Make follow-up calls within the prescribed number of days. Don't expect to conduct business on a resume that was sent months or even weeks ago.

6) When leaving messages make sure they are focused and to-the-point. Stay away from long and overly explanatory voice mail and secretary messages. Don't become a pain by leaving too many messages. Try to get direct line numbers and call at times when the hiring authority may answer the phone: Early/late in the work day, or just before/after the lunch hour.

7) When following-up, aim for firm, "yes" or "no" responses from the employer. If there is an interest in your background, build your marketing plan and then set up an interview.

8) Capitalize on rejection! If the employer has no interest or position, ask for a referral to another potential hiring source. If you don't ask, the response will be "NO" 100% of the time.

9) Once referred, move into action with an "immediate action telephone call." DON'T WAIT! Call the referral immediately. Establish connectivity (the common link between you and them) and be prepared to present your 20-second

commercial. Determine if there is or isn't an interest and proceed with the proper RMF responses.

10) All referrals are put back into the RMF system for interviews or referral to another source. Continue the system until you have been offered and you have accepted the job of your choice.

These goals are now your goals. Read them, remember them, refer back to them.

Now that you've identified your 10 Job Search Goals, Chapter 3 will show you how to accomplish them.

"Things may come to those who wait,
but only the things left by those who hustled."
A. Lincoln

CHAPTER THREE

THE RMF SYSTEM

This system was developed to:

1) assist you in organizing your job search.
2) give you a plan which takes advantage of every resume and cover letter you send.
3) give you the resume "volume power" you need without the impersonal and reactive nature of mass mailing.
4) teach you how to build and expand your job search network.
5) give you greater access to the "hidden job market."
6) assist you to identify and apply job search goals that yield success.
7) help you establish follow-up actions which lead to more interviews and referrals.
8) allow you to capitalize on rejection.
9) assist you in your company research.
10) assemble a job search campaign that nets results.

The RMF system is composed of three phases. Research, Mail and Follow-up. Begin with the Research phase.

Research Phase (R)

In the research phase you will be identifying and researching the companies to whom you wish to apply. This information will allow you to build meaningful prospecting cover letters. Your individually created prospecting letter, along with your resume, will then be sent to each organization to which you apply.

In this phase of your job search, you will be researching basic information needed to make initial contact with an employer. This information will also assist you while making follow-up telephone calls.

Initial contact information includes:

ORGANIZATION NAME — Proper spelling with no abbreviations.

CONTACT NAME/TITLE — Preferably a hiring authority. Correct spelling and title. Work with Human Resources only if you can not identify the hiring authority.

Hiring Authority — A hiring manager directing the operational area/department in which you wish to work, usually one or two position levels above the one for which you are applying. This person has the ability to make a hiring decision concerning you.

Though Personnel and Human Resources Departments are involved in and are an integral part of the hiring process, they are only considered hiring authorities for positions within their own Operational Department. Apply through the Human Resources Department only if you cannot identify the hiring authority for the position you are applying for.

Many job seekers have a preconceived idea that obtaining the name of a hiring authority is a very difficult task. It usually isn't. Remember you don't need, or necessarily want, to talk to the hiring authority during the research phase (that will take place in follow-up). In the research phase, identify the hiring authority, and obtain the proper spelling of his/her name and full title.

To obtain that name, begin by calling the organization. Tell the receptionist (or whoever answers the phone) that you are sending information to ______________________ (proper title/level, one or two positions above the one you are applying for) and you need that person's name and title.

Example: (for software engineer)
"Hello, can you please help me. I'm sending some information to your Manager of Software Engineering, could you please give me the proper spelling of that person's name and full title?"

Do not give the receptionist your life history, or say that you are looking for work. It is unnecessary and potentially prevents you from accomplishing your goals! If you do, you will likely be dispatched to the Human Resources Department with due haste.

If the receptionist is unable to identify the proposed title you request, become more descriptive; help the receptionist assist you.

Example:
"Then can you please tell me who is in charge of designing and developing software for your company. That person probably works in the engineering department."

If the person to whom you are speaking is still unable to assist you, ask to be transferred to a secretary/receptionist in the engineering department.

Example:
"Can you please transfer me to the Engineering Department, I'm sure someone there will be able to help me."

If all efforts fail to get this information about the hiring authority, identification of the Human Resources Manager is the next logical step.

ADDRESS — Correct spelling with zip codes. If there are multiple locations, make sure to send your resume/cover letter to the correct one.

TELEPHONE NUMBER — Get direct line phone number of hiring authority if possible. Direct line numbers will assist you later when doing follow-ups (ask the receptionist when you call to identify the hiring authority).

FAX NUMBER — Just in case you need it.

NOTES — Basic information you should research prior to applying.

What Information Should You Research Prior to Applying?

Here is basic information that you should know when applying for a position.

Is there a current job opening for the type of position you seek?

Is there an available job description? (If so try and get a copy)

What helpful and insightful information can you gather from advertisements, other published information (be it current or dated), or through networking?

If there is no position advertised, how might you fit into the company?

What kind of position might you fill that would also be fulfilling for you?

How could you make a meaningful contribution and assist the organization in accomplishing its goals?

What experience or skills might be needed for the position?

How should you market yourself to show a compatible match with the needs of the organization?

What professional qualifications, licenses, degrees or other training would make you an asset to the firm?

What are the company's products or services?

How long has the company been in business?

Where are the company's other plants, stores, offices located? How many are there?

What is the company's financial position and are they making a profit? For non-profits: What is the source of their funding?

Is the organization experiencing growth, and what are its prospects for future growth?

If you can answer these questions, you are well on your way to understanding the employer.

Where to Conduct Your Research

An entire book could be written on this subject alone. This text will not attempt to completely address the issue of research but will give you a partial list of places where you can get started.

To begin conducting research on publicly owned firms, consult:

- ❑ Compact Disclosure (CD Rom Product, in many reference libraries)
- ❑ Million Dollar Directory (Duns)
- ❑ S&P Register of Corporations, Directors and Executives
- ❑ Thomas Register
- ❑ Annual Reports
- ❑ Value line Investment Survey
- ❑ Computerized indexes such as, Wall Street Journal Index, National Computerized Newspaper/Magazine Indexes, Business Periodical Index, Newsbank Electronic Index. (Many of these indexes can be found in major public, college/university libraries).
- ❑ S&P Industry Survey
- ❑ U.S. Industrial Outlook

To begin doing research on subsidiaries and divisions of companies, consult:

- ❑ Directory of Corporate Affiliations
- ❑ American Corporate Families
- ❑ Who Owns Whom
- ❑ Computerized Newspaper/Magazine Indexes

To begin doing research on foreign owned companies, consult:

- ❑ Directory of Foreign Manufacturers in the U.S.
- ❑ Directory of Foreign Investments in the U.S.
- ❑ Moody's International Manual
- ❑ Directory of International Enterprises
- ❑ Business International Index
- ❑ Computerized Newspaper/Magazine Indexes

To begin doing research on privately held companies, consult:

- ❑ Directory of Leading Private Companies
- ❑ Computerized Newspaper/Magazine Indexes

Information on privately held firms can be difficult to research. If all efforts fail at the reference library, call the company and ask them to send you current information about their products/services and their history. An excellent source on researching companies (and my source) can be found in, *How to Research Companies*, by Karmen Crowther, *Job Choices*, Planning Edition, National Association of Employers and Colleges, 1996; pages 23-28.

If you can't find all, or any, information about a firm to whom you wish to apply and you have given research your best shot, APPLY ANYWAY and base your candidacy on whatever data you have been able to uncover.

The Internet

The Internet is an incredible source of information that you can utilize in your job search. Not only does it contain reference, historical and financial data about companies, but there are also many job postings. Apply the internet to the RMF System as you would any published source or computerized index in the Research Phase (as a source to both identifying companies that are actively seeking candidates and prospecting). Here are a few Internet sources you might investigate. This list does not even begin to scratch the surface, and this is a source well worth investigating.

- ❑ Monster Board
  http://www.monster.com/
- ❑ Online Career Center
  http://www.iquest.net/occ/
- ❑ Federal Job Opportunities Bulletin Board
  fjob.mail.opgov
- ❑ Career Mosaic
  www.careermosaic.com/infoseek.htnl

To find job boards and career center postings and other helpful sources try this web address.

- ❑ http://www.yahoo.com/business_and_economy/employment/careers

Building Prospecting Cover Letters

You are now ready to build your prospecting cover letter(s) based on the information you have gathered from research.

"Prospecting Cover Letter(s)" are used, along with your resume, to express interest in an organization, demonstrate that your research has determined there may be a potential employment match (even though the organization is not currently advertising), and uncover and apply for positions that either are not being advertised or are in the process of being created. These letters, along with your resume, allow you to access the hidden job market.

Here are some basics to keep in mind while building your prospecting cover letters.

- ❑ Refer to a style guide and become familiar with the look, structure and punctuation of a block style business letter
- ❑ Keep your letters warm yet professional
- ❑ Keep them to one page
- ❑ Make sure they reflect individual interest in the position/company (canned, mass-mailed letters are usually quite apparent even to the unschooled reader. These letters don't usually accomplish their mission)
- ❑ Address them to individuals: NEVER ADDRESS A LETTER "To Whom It May Concern," and avoid "Attention: Human Resources Manager"
- ❑ Letters should be well organized with proper punctuation and grammar and no spelling errors
- ❑ Letters should be career and skills centered, never self-centered. "Me" issues such as salary requirements, benefit needs, or your own personal expectations have no place in your cover letter

Many sources are available to assist you in building these letters. Your university career library more than likely has excellent examples to help you fashion your own letter, but please don't copy someone else's work.

Here are a few guidelines and examples of what might be found in a basic three paragraph cover letter.

Paragraph 1:
Explain why you are writing the letter and your objective. This paragraph can also explain how you identified the position or the company and the research that has prompted you to apply. Research is especially important when developing a prospecting cover letter.

An introductory paragraph for a prospecting cover letter might begin in this manner.

Example:
I have recently been conducting research and investigating major corporations that are manufacturers of pharmaceuticals in the Phoenix area. My research has documented ____(the company)____ unequaled leadership for over 25 years in the areas of new product development and customer service. It is with the highest degree of enthusiasm that I write this letter to inquire about positions on your sales team.

Paragraph 2:
Answer these questions:

What background and experiences qualify you for this position?

How do you fit in?

How can you make a contribution?

Discuss how the requirements of the position match the **skills** you can bring to their firm.

Skills will vary from position to position (required skills for an accountant would be quite different from those of a fire fighter). Refer to such resources as the *Occupational Outlook Handbook,* SIGI Plus (computer assisted guidance program by Educational Testing Services), The Dictionary of Occupational Titles, company job descriptions, or other reference materials to determine the skills you should address in paragraph two of your letter. These books and the software program are found at many public libraries and university/community college career centers.

Example:
I am a recent graduate of ________________________ University with a Bachelor of Science in Marketing. While attending the University I was able to maintain a 3.75 GPA while working between 25-30 hours per week. I am also very active in many on and off campus activities and was recently elected to a leadership position in the student chapter of the American Marketing Association. My current internship is in the sales and marketing department of a major manufacturer of health care products. This internship has helped me solidify my career goals and enabled me to gain valuable training from experienced professionals in the health care industry. This position also afforded me the opportunity to further develop the technical, communication, and interpersonal skills necessary for a successful career in sales. I am certain that my experience, academic preparation, and personal determination to succeed will allow me to make a major contribution to your sales team.

Paragraph 3:
Ask for an interview. Facilitate contact by providing a telephone number at which you can be easily reached. Thank them for their time and consideration and use, "Sincerely" as your closing.

Example:
Please consider my request for a personal interview. If you should have any questions concerning my resume, please feel free to contact me at (555) 555-5555. I look forward to meeting with you in the near future. Thank you for your time and consideration.

Sincerely,

(your signature)

name typed

Remember to make all your letters individualized to the company and position. Always, always, always make them "contribution" oriented, never "what's in it for me" oriented.

You are now ready to attach your cover letter(s) to your resume(s) and get them in the mail.

Followed-up Resume Volume Power

Trickling two or three resumes into the job market every 30 to 40 days does not position the odds of finding employment in your favor. A degree of resume volume must be introduced into the job market to conduct a successful job search.

Sending out 10 to 15 cover letters and resumes every 10 to 15 days is a realistic and attainable goal. From this time on, it is your resume volume goal.

This type of "followed-up resume volume power" allows you to do proper research, identify hiring authorities, write individualized cover letters, and make follow-up phone calls.

Do not send hundreds of resumes at one time. Flooding the market with your paperwork usually leads to minimal follow-up. Consistent follow-up is one of the most important goals in your job search plan.

If you shotgun mass quantities of resumes into the market place, it can be guaranteed that your follow-up will become impossible, your research will be non-existent, and you will stop dealing with people who can truly have a positive effect on your job search, e.g., hiring authorities.

Flow Chart For the Research Phase

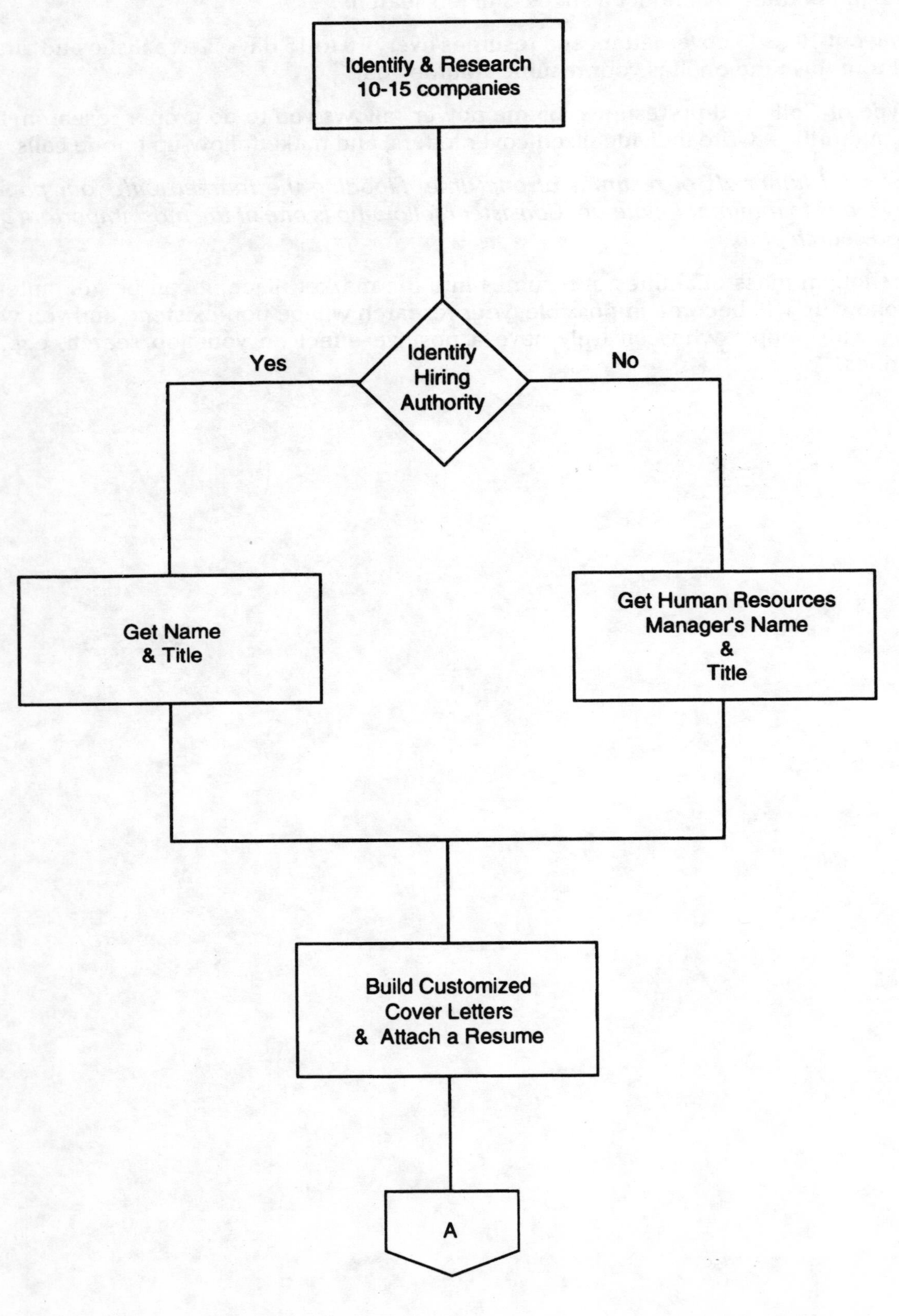

The Mail Phase (M)

In the mail phase you'll send out your resumes and cover letters, anticipate their approximate day of arrival, and prepare to conduct your follow-up telephone calls. It is also the time when you'll begin to research your next group of 10 to 15 organizations. Every time you enter the mail phase, you will also recommence the research phase.

Here is a geometric model of the RMF System demonstrating how the research and mail phase go hand-in-hand. Using this system maximizes your time and delivers the followed-up resume volume power your job search needs (resume group = 10 to 15 resumes).

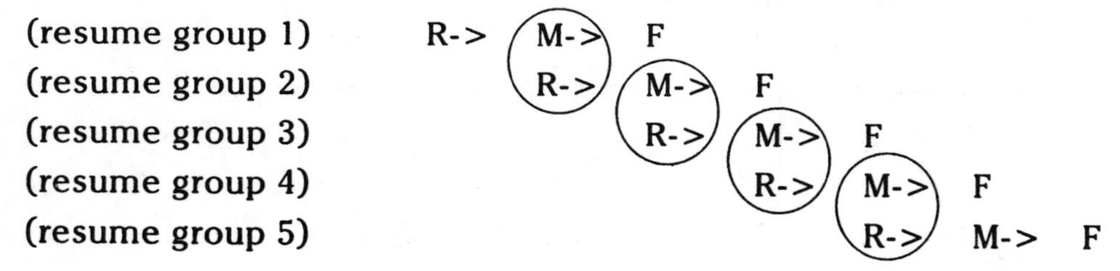

Job Search Downtime Is Deadly

Job search downtime kills. Do not anticipate that a second interview will lead to a job offer. Don't stop your search because an employer tells you that an employment offer is pending or a reference check is in-process. Always have a new group of resumes and cover letters prepared to enter the job market no matter how strongly an opportunity seems to appear at the moment. Don't stop searching until the day you accept a firm offer (and get a letter to confirm it)!

If you are unemployed and seriously seeking work, job search downtime is absolutely unacceptable!

Rejection Letters

When a job seeker shows me a stack of rejection letters, it usually confirms that he/she is not moving from the mail phase to the follow-up phase soon enough or is not conducting follow-up at all.

Firms in close proximity to your geographic location should receive your resume in a few days. Out-of-state firms (geographically distant) will receive them within a business week. Give the company a day to get your resume into the hands of the hiring authority before you move to the follow-up phase.

Don't wait two or three weeks before conducting follow-up telephone calls. This type of untimely or "slack" follow-up increases your risk of becoming lost in the shuffle and decreases your chances of securing an interview. Waiting two to three weeks to follow-up on your resume will insure that it has become a doily for a potted plant, a chew toy for an employer's pet, or a coaster for a coffee cup.

Slack follow-up increases your chances of receiving rejection letters by mail. Rejection letters are unproductive; they negatively effect your attitude, confidence, and self-esteem, and they prevent you from accomplishing your job search goals.

Go to the Follow-up Phase before you can be rejected through the mail. If you are to be rejected, I want you to be rejected on the telephone while speaking with the employer!

I realize that this idea sounds outlandish, but as you will discover, capitalizing on rejection is an important part of your job search.

Flow Chart For the Mail Phase

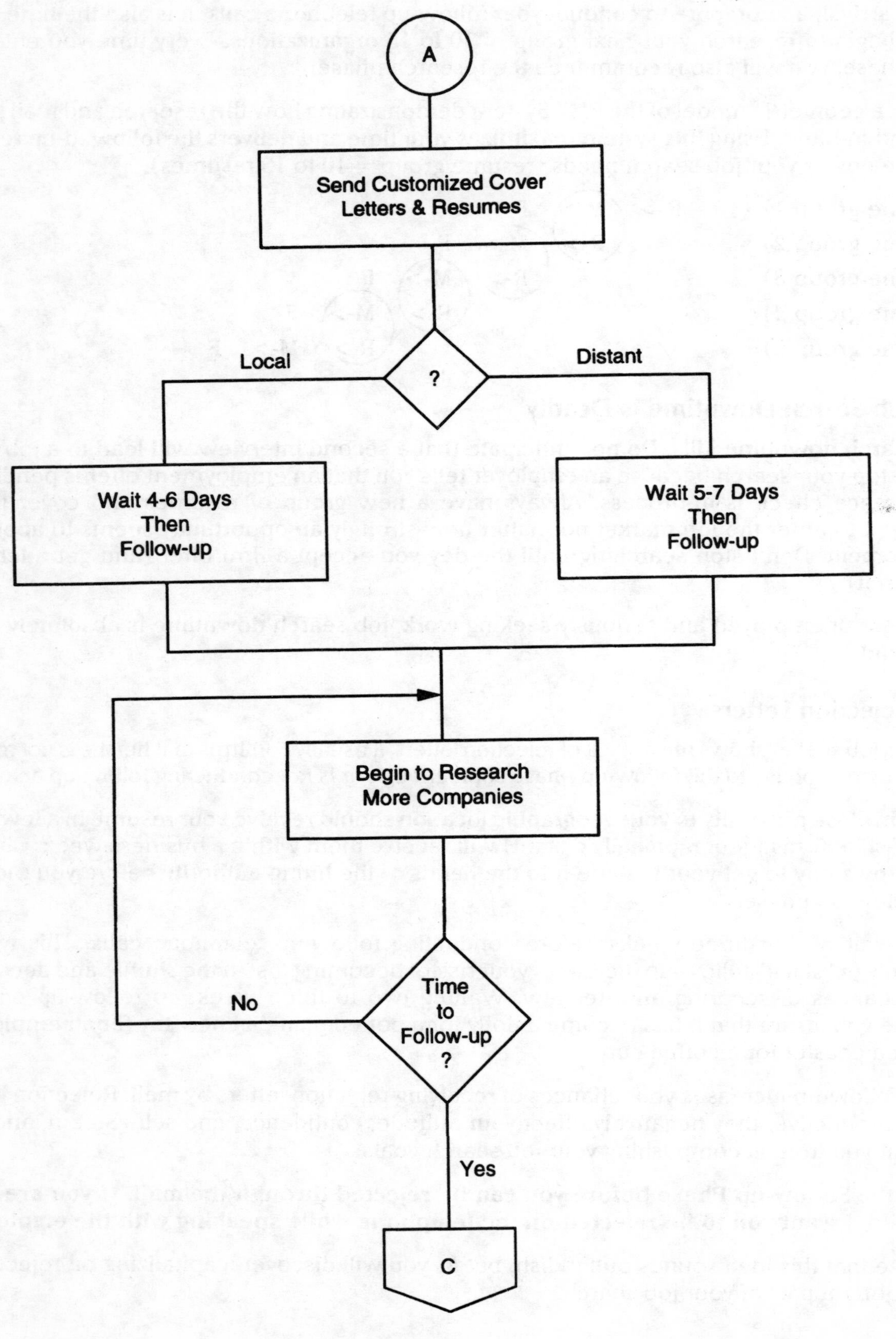

The Follow-Up Phase (F)

After waiting the prescribed number of days for the employers to receive your resume, you are ready to move to the follow-up phase. Follow-up includes initiating contact by calling EACH employer to whom you have sent your resume and cover letter, introducing yourself through a short presentation, and querying the employers interest in you.

Your Initial Follow-up Conversation with the Employer

Begin your initial conversations with the employer by:

1) Introducing yourself.
2) Establishing a connection. This connection could be from interest created from company research, referral from a mutual acquaintance, friend, referring employer, etc.
3) Describing yourself with a short but dynamic summary of your background, applicable skills, education and experiences—otherwise known as a **20-second commercial.**
4) Asking if they have received and reviewed your letter and resume.
5) Determining if there is an interest in your background.
6) Eliciting a clear YES or NO interest answer from the employer.

Introducing Yourself and Creating Your Own 20-Second Commercial

Here are examples of three introductory telephone conversations that are based on how you might have initiated contact.

1) Answering a published advertisement
2) Prospecting for a position
3) Initial contact from a referral

Example 1:
Introductory follow-up conversation with 20-second commercial, used when answering a published advertisement.

Hello, Mr./Ms. __________, My name is ____________________________________. May I have a moment of your time?

I recently sent my resume to you concerning the position of _______________ that was advertised in the December 10th issue of ________________________. After reviewing the position, I determined that it was an excellent fit for my skills and qualifications.

You might recall from my resume that I'm a degreed ________________ with _____ years experience in ____. I'm calling to find out if you've had an opportunity to review my resume and determine if there is interest in my background.

Example 2:

Introductory follow-up conversation with 20-second commercial, used when prospecting for a position.

Hello, Mr./Ms. _____ my name is ____________. May I have a moment of your time?

I recently sent you my resume. I'm a graduate of ______________ university with a degree in ____________. You might also recall that I had an internship in the __________ department of a major ____________ company, and was the president of the student chapter of the American Marketing Association.

I'm calling to find out if you had the opportunity to review this information and determine if there is an interest in my background.

Example 3:

Introductory follow-up conversation with 20-second commercial, used when you have been referred.

Hello, Mr. Jones, My name is _____________. May I have a moment of your time?

Mr./Ms. ____________ referred your name to me and said that I should contact you immediately. He/she mentioned that you might be in the process of expanding your tax department and could be looking for a staff accountant.

I am a recent graduate of_________________ with a master's degree in accounting. I also have two years of experience working with a big six accounting firm as a staff accountant in their tax division.

I'm calling to find out if that position, or any other accounting positions, might be opening within your organization.

Learning to present yourself over the telephone is an important job search skill. Practice with a friend or an advisor and get some feedback. You may decide to initially script yourself until you feel comfortable enough to present your own 20-second commercial without hesitation.

Three Probable Follow-up Scenarios

There is a very high probability that you will encounter one of three potential scenarios when following-up with an employer. In your follow-up, anticipate hearing one of these three answers and prepare to take the appropriate action necessary for you to accomplish your job search goals.

1) Yes, there is an interest.
2) No interest or no position.
3) Employer has not seen or cannot find your resume.

What To Do When an Employer Says: Yes, There Is an Interest!

Many job-seekers, upon hearing that an employer has an interest in their background, make the common mistake of immediately setting up an interview time and then scurrying off the phone.

After all, they have accomplished what they set forth to do, get an interview. But the unfortunate part about this scenario is that the applicant is going to be interviewed for positions of which they have little or no knowledge or understanding.

In the interview they hope to put together a cogent and thoughtful presentation, showing how their skills match the needs of the position, without knowing the duties and responsibilities of the job. However, the interview is hardly the ideal time or place to try and figure out how the wants and needs of the company match one's skills and abilities. That should be done well before the interview takes place!

Now, just before setting up your interview appointment, is the time to find out more about the position and build your marketing plan! Who would be a better person to ask questions concerning the position than the person who is doing the hiring?

Review the position with that person! Ask for an up-to-date job description. Find out as much as you can and build a plan to market yourself to the employer.

It's not enough to just get the interview—that's only the first step; now you must become the best prepared candidate and get the job offer.

Employers usually hire the best prepared candidates,
not the best qualified ones.

Information, research, introspection and preparation will make you the best prepared candidate.

How to Build Your Marketing Plan

Example of questions you might ask an employer when building your marketing plan:

"That sounds great. Can you please tell me more about the position?"

"What is the title of the position?"

"Who would this person report to (get the name and title)?"

"What are the duties and responsibilities of the position? (what skills/experience is required)"

"Do you have an up-to-date job description that I might have access to?"

"Is there anything else you might be able to tell me about the position?"

Setting Up the Interview

Here are some examples of responses that will assist you in setting-up an interview.

The position sounds very interesting! When can we get together and discuss this in greater detail?

(Give the person an opportunity to suggest a time; if he/she does not, proceed to the next question)

Would this Thursday, the 22nd, work for you? Would 9 a.m. be a good time for you?

(Take the initiative and propose a date and time. Remember, the sooner the better. However, you may try and avoid scheduling interviews on Monday mornings or late on Friday afternoons. Fridays, a.m. or p.m., prior to a long holiday weekend can also be very distracting days for employers.)

Verify the address and location of the interview, especially if there are multiple facilities. If you are uncertain about the location, **GET DIRECTIONS**. Arriving 20 minutes late for your interview is not considered fashionable, and will not earn any points for you.

What to Do When an Employer Says: There Is No Position or No Interest

If there is no interest or no position available for you at this time, *always, always, always ask for a referral to another potential hiring source, either within or outside the company.*

If you are going to be rejected, let it take place over the telephone where you can ask for a referral. Most job seekers think that the only way they can succeed in a job search is to wait near the telephone, hoping that the company employment office will call to invite them in for an interview. This is a reactive, low percentage job hunting technique, and certainly not one that you can afford to use. By taking a proactive approach, you give yourself more options to succeed.

Capitalize on Rejection

Though no one relishes being personally rejected over the telephone, doing so increases your odds of uncovering positions in the hidden market place.

Being rejected over the telephone gives you the opportunity to expand your network by asking for a referral to another potential employer.

If you are working with hiring authorities, you are dealing with individuals who are networked.

Hiring authorities have worked at other companies, have friends who work at other companies, and are associated with professional societies and organizations. Take advantage of their knowledge and tap into their network.

Seek a referral every time you are rejected! Many of these referrals will be to unadvertised positions in the "Hidden Job Market."

Since the hidden job market is estimated to contain many more positions than the published marketplace, access to these positions is critically important to your job search.

The Hiring Ladder

Being referred through a related source enhances the perception of your employment candidacy to the subsequent employer.

What "Rung of the Hiring Ladder" are you on? or How does an employer perceive your employment candidacy?

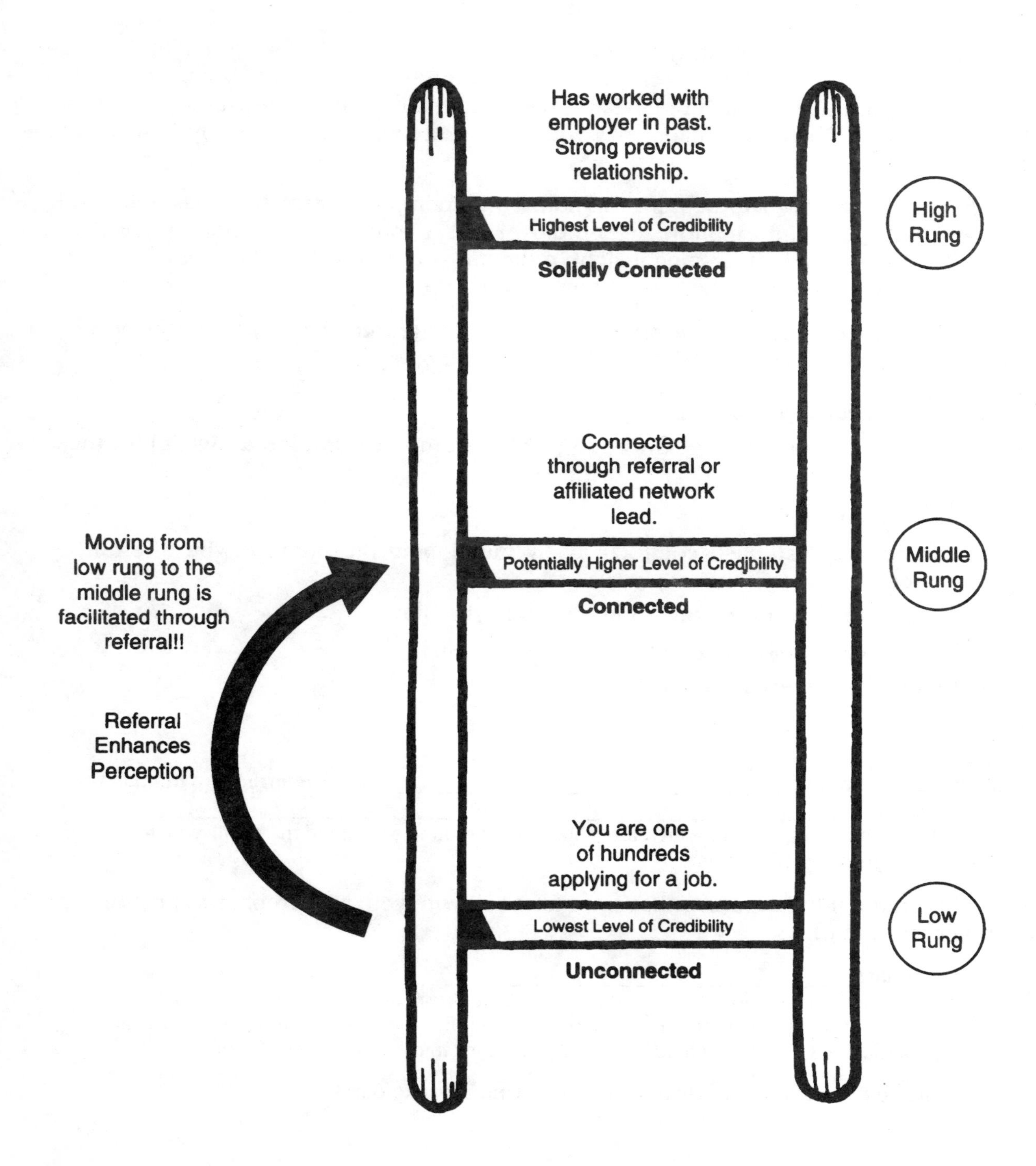

Referral to positions in the hidden job market is an important element in a successful job search!

How to Ask the Employer for a Referral

This is actually quite simple. Once the employer has rejected you, ask this question:

> Mr./Ms.__________________. Thank you very much for your time and consideration. May I ask one final question? Do you know of anyone who might potentially have an interest in my background? I'd greatly appreciate any referrals you might be able to give me.

Some job hunters fear that they may receive an angry reaction or further rejection from an employer if they venture to ask for a referral. However, the potential risk of being confronted with this type of normally unusual behavior is well worth the potential rewards of a referral into the "hidden job market." In reality, once you have been rejected, you have nothing to lose by asking for a referral.

Do everything in your power to acquire the name/title, company name, address, telephone number, and any other information the employer has about the referred company and position. This will assist you in gaining insight to the job and putting together your 20-second commercial for presentation to the referred employer.

Always ask if you can use the referring employer's name as the source of connectivity (referral); this will assist you in moving up to the middle rung of the hiring ladder.

Immediate Action Telephone Call

When you win a referral take immediate action. Call the employer **immediately**! Follow these steps:

1) Identify yourself
2) Immediately establish connectivity by mentioning the name of the referral source
3) Ask the employer for a few moments of his/her time
4) Present your 20-second commercial
5) Determine if there is an interest

Example:

> Ms. Smith, my name is ______________________________. I was referred by a mutual acquaintance, ________________________ from ________________________. S/he told me that you might have an interest in my background and urged me to call you. May I have a few minutes of your time?

(pause to determine if the employer has time to speak with you, and prepare to present your 20-second commercial)

> I'm a graduate of ______________________________ University with a degree in accounting. I also have two years of internship with a big six accounting firm, and another year of basic bookkeeping with a small manufacturing firm. While attending school I was able to maintain a 3.5 GPA and held leadership positions in my professional fraternity.
>
> I'm calling to find out if you might have an interest in my background.

If the employer does not have time to discuss this matter now, establish a date and time to do so.

If the referred employer has an interest, return to **YES, THERE IS AN INTEREST**, build your marketing plan and set up an interview. If the employer asks for a resume, determine the most expeditious method of providing one and establish a follow-up date and time. Dropping the resume off along with a scheduled appointment to personally meet with the employer at the business address is ideal. Sounds like an interview doesn't it!

If the employer has no interest or position, return to **NO, THERE IS NO INTEREST OR POSITION**, and ask for a referral. Place all names back into the RMF system and make an immediate action telephone call to the referred employer.

Know When You Are Being Told No

Accepting vague explanations will get you nowhere, referrals will!

Below are examples of answers that usually get you nowhere:

1) Call me back in a few months; we hope to have openings then.
2) We will keep your resume in our files and call you if something opens up.
3) I've forwarded it to the Human Resources Department; they will call you when we have positions open.

Rejection and a referral are of much greater benefit to a job seeker than a gentle brush-off by a disinterested employer. From this point forward, rejection equals referral.

What Should You Do if You Are Having Trouble Getting the Names of Referrals from the Employers?

This is a common challenge. In some cases employers prefer to initiate contact with the referral prior to giving out their name.

Ostensibly this sounds like a good plan, but it's probably not. It takes all control out of when, where, and how contact is made. You are the one with the vested interest in finding a job, not the employer making the referral. You have no way of knowing if the actual contact will ever be made or how impressively your skills and qualifications will be presented, unless you do it.

Urge the employer to give you the referral information so you can make the contact. If the employer will not, establish a follow-up date and time (usually within three to five days) for you to call them back, just in case the referred employer has not contacted you. If the employer has forgotten to make the contact, strongly urge him/her to share the information with you so you can make this important contact.

What to Do if the Employer Has Not Seen or Cannot Find Your Resume

For geographically local employers:
Ask if you may drop the resume off at a specified date and time. Also ask if you will have an opportunity to meet them when the resume is delivered. Be flexible and be accommodating to the employer's schedule.

If the employer expresses interest, build your marketing plan and set up a confirmed appointment time.

If the employer dissuades your dropping off the resume and says that there is no interest or position, ask for a referral.

For geographically distant employers:
Ask for the employer's fax number and establish a time and date to follow-up on your resume.

Overnight mail is also a viable and potentially stronger method of making immediate contact with an employer. Overnight mail is normally considered a "higher priority," open-me-first item. It also allows you to use a resume and cover letter which was produced on a finer quality of paper than that used by most fax machines. If the employer has no interest or position, ask for a referral.

Leaving Follow-up Messages

If the employer you are trying to reach is not returning your messages, there could be good reasons, many of which might not be due to a lack of interest. It is possible the person is out of town, on vacation, or involved in meetings or other activities that prevent timely call-backs.

Any message that you leave for an employer should be friendly, well thought out and professionally presented.

If the first impression you create for the employer is six or seven increasingly disoriented and irate voice mail messages, I guarantee that you will not receive a return call.

Leave no more than three to four unanswered messages. If you call more than that prescribed number, don't leave messages. Leaving copious and repetitive follow-up messages quickly changes your employment status from viable candidate to unwanted nuisance.

Try calling direct numbers or calling at times when the employer might personally answer the telephone. Early in the morning, just before or after lunch, and end of working hours are potential times for this to happen.

Resume Blocking

Resume blocking is a technique used especially if you are conducting a geographically distant job search. When mailing a group of 10 to 15 resumes send them all to the same general geographic area. Resume blocking can help you get more referrals in your desired location and save money you would spend on travel arrangements because:

- ❑ referrals will often be to other opportunities within that same geographic area.
- ❑ if a company expresses interest but will not pay for travel or overnight stay expenses, you may identify another in that group of resumes that will (piggy-backing interviews in this fashion can make a great difference in a long distance job search especially when you have limited funds).

Be Persistent

Persistence is the key. Don't give up. Stick to your job search goals. You only have to find one good job. Follow the RMF system until you find the position that fits your needs.

"I will persist until I succeed."
Og Mandino from *The Worlds Greatest Salesman*

Flow Chart For the Follow-up Phase

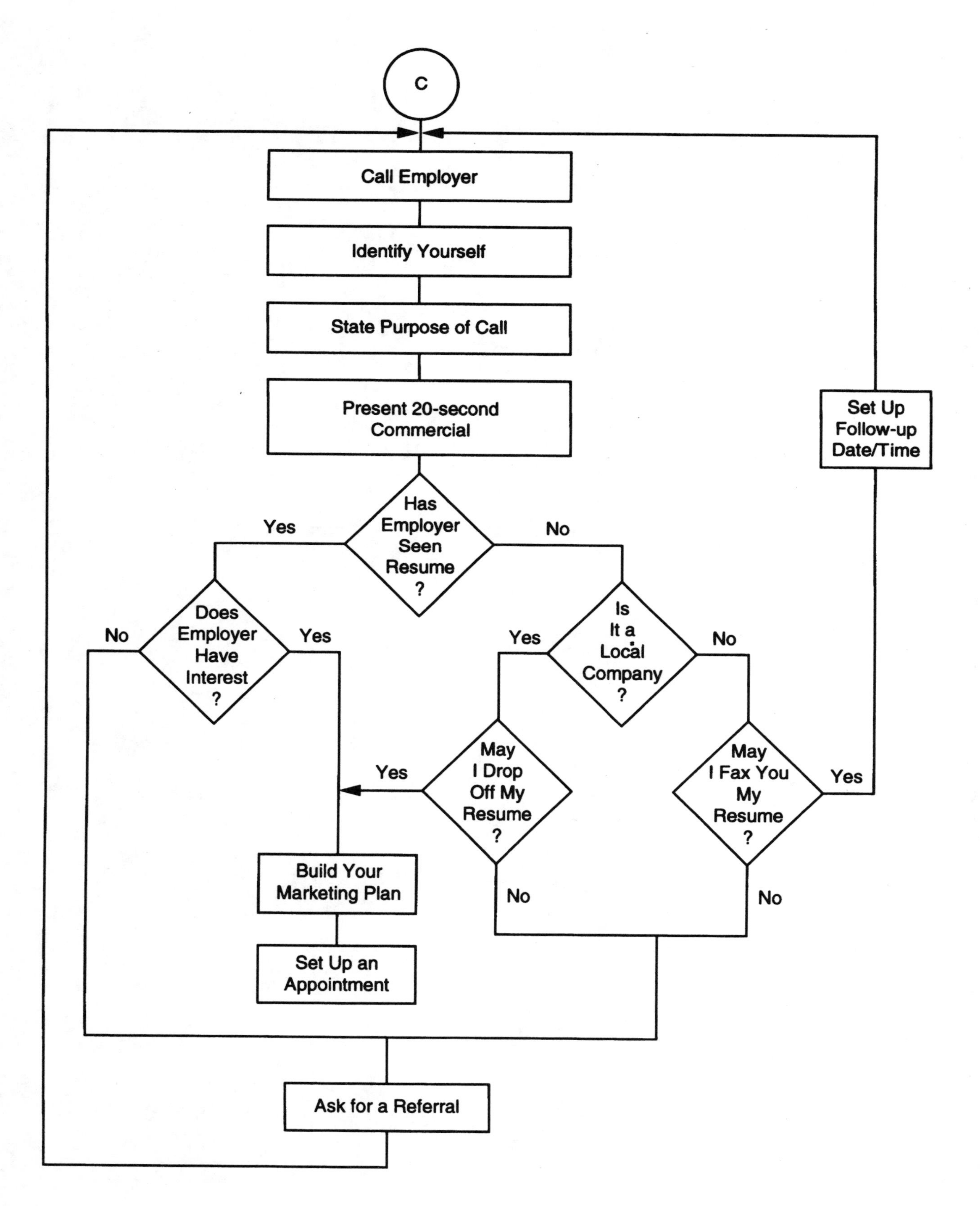

Chapter Four

The RMF Contact Form

How to Use the RMF Employer Contact Form

Your workbook contains **60** RMF EMPLOYER CONTACT FORMS. Use one work sheet for each company you wish to apply to. These forms facilitate the RMF System by:

- helping you gather/organize information
- keeping track of the employer to whom you have applied
- aiding in your follow-up conversations

Take out an RMF work sheet and become familiar with it.

Page 1 contains sections marked:

CONTACT DATES:

Date mailed: The date your resume was sent to the employer.

Anticipated follow-up date: The date you plan to place a follow-up phone call to the employer.

Actual follow-up date: The date you initiate your first follow-up phone call to the employer (subsequent dates/times located below in follow-up phase of Contact Form).

RESEARCH PHASE: Refer back to pages 15–22.

MAIL PHASE: Refer back to pages 23–24.

FOLLOW-UP PHASE: Refer back to pages 25–33.

Page 2 contains the FOLLOW-UP ACTION PLAN with sections marked:

YES, THERE IS AN INTEREST: Refer back to pages 26–27.

NO INTEREST OR NO POSITION: Refer back to pages 28–31.

HAS NOT SEEN RESUME: Refer back to pages 31–32.

Examples of the RMF Employer Contact Form are included in the following pages. Each example demonstrates one of the Probable Follow-up Scenarios discussed in Chapter 3. If you are experiencing any difficulty when filling out the Contact Forms, consult Chapter 3.

Follow the system. Follow-up and referral are essential! Stick to your goals and take control of your job search.

*Example: Follow-up with **Yes, There Is an Interest** employer response.*

RMF Employer Contact Form

Contact Dates:
Date mailed: 1/15/96 Anticipated follow-up date 1/19/96
Actual follow-up date 1/20/96

★ ★ ★ ★ ★

Research Phase:
Organization's Name: XYZ Corporation
Contact Name/Title: Tom Smith, Marketing Manager
Address: 26 XYZ Lane
Tempe, AZ 85257
Telephone Number: (602) 555-5575 Fax Number: (602) 555-5576
Notes:
Job posted in ASU's Career Center. Fresh grad, willing to train, seeks strong communication, interpersonal skills. Prior internship a plus. Co. manufactures test equipment. Est. 1978, has 250 employees. $75mm in Sales 1994.

Build your cover letter based on the research you have conducted. Place your letter along with your resume in the mail and move to the Mail Phase.

★ ★ ★ ★ ★

Mail Phase:
For geographically local companies, wait 4 to 6 days and then proceed to the Follow-up Phase.
For geographically distant companies wait 5 to 7 days and then proceed to the Follow-up Phase.
Begin doing research on more companies.

★ ★ ★ ★ ★

Follow-up Phase:
Place telephone call to the employer.

1) Introduce yourself
2) Tell purpose of phone call
3) Present 20-second commercial
4) Determine if there is an interest
5) Go to back of contact form and follow appropriate follow-up action.

Messages:
Date/Time: 1/20/96 10:00 am
Date/Time: 1/22/96 11:45 am
Date/Time: ____________

Secretary's name ____________

★ ★ ★

FOLLOW-UP ACTION:

☒ **Yes, There Is an Interest:**

Build your marketing plan by gathering as much information as you can about the position. Take notes!

Position/title: Marketing Assistant

Position reports to: Tom Smith

Skills/experience required:
marketing degree, strong interpersonal & communication skills. Stressed use of computers (not in Job Listing) Excel & dbase now important. Will conduct marketing surveys and analyze data.

Interview date/time: 1/26/96 – 10:00 am – Ask for Tom

Directions: North East Corner of University Drive and XYZ Lane.

★ ★ ★

❑ **No Interest or No Position:**

Ask for a referral!

Name of referred company: ____________________

Name/title of referred employer: ____________________

Address: ____________________
____
____

Telephone Number: ____________________

★ ★ ★

❑ **Has Not Seen Resume:**

Geographically local employer — Suggest that you drop off the resume at a specified date and time. If employer says yes, proceed to ❑ **Yes, There Is an Interest** and build your marketing plan and set up an appointment. If employer responds by saying no interest or nothing open, proceed to ❑ **No Interest or No Position** and ask for a referral.

Geographically distant employer — Establish most expeditious method of sending information to employer with follow-up date and time.

Follow-up date/time: ____________________

If there is no interest or position, ask for a referral.

Example: Follow-up with ***No Interest or No Position*** *response from employer.*
Referral given.

RMF Employer Contact Form

Contact Dates:
Date mailed: 1/15/96 Anticipated follow-up date 1/20/96
Actual follow-up date 1/21/96

☆ ☆ ☆ ☆ ☆

Research Phase:
Organization's Name: ABC Incorporated
Contact Name/Title: Tina Jones, Software Engineering Mgr.
Address: 32 ABC Lane
Scottsdale, AZ 85258
Telephone Number: (602) 555-1919 Fax Number: (602) 555-1633
Notes: Prospected company from Phoenix Job Bank. Company established 1988 – manufactures machine controls. Sales for 1994 – $6 mm. Job Bank says they design state-of-the-art controls and often seek qualified engineers.

Build your cover letter based on the research you have conducted. Place your letter along with your resume in the mail and move to the Mail Phase.

☆ ☆ ☆ ☆ ☆

Mail Phase:
For geographically local companies, wait 4 to 6 days and then proceed to the Follow-up Phase.
For geographically distant companies wait 5 to 7 days and then proceed to the Follow-up Phase.
Begin doing research on more companies.

☆ ☆ ☆ ☆ ☆

Follow-up Phase:
Place telephone call to the employer.

1) Introduce yourself
2) Tell purpose of phone call
3) Present 20-second commercial
4) Determine if there is an interest
5) Go to back of contact form and follow appropriate follow-up action.

Messages:
Date/Time: 1/21/96 9:30 am
Date/Time: ______
Date/Time: ______

Secretary's name ______

★ ★ ★

Follow-up Action:

❑ **Yes, There Is an Interest:**

Build your marketing plan by gathering as much information as you can about the position. Take notes!

Position/title: ______________________________

Position reports to: ______________________________

Skills/experience required:

Interview date/time: ______________________________

Directions:

★ ★ ★

☒ **No Interest or No Position:**

Ask for a referral!

Name of referred company: Jones Engineering

Name/title of referred employer: Ted Simmons, Design manager

Address: 875 Western Parkway
Phoenix, AZ 83636

Telephone Number: (602) 555-4444

★ ★ ★

❑ **Has Not Seen Resume:**

Geographically local employer — Suggest that you drop off the resume at a specified date and time. If employer says yes, proceed to ❑ **Yes, There Is an Interest** and build your marketing plan and set up an appointment. If employer responds by saying no interest or nothing open, proceed to ❑ **No Interest or No Position** and ask for a referral.

Geographically distant employer — Establish most expeditious method of sending information to employer with follow-up date and time.

Follow-up date/time: ____________________

If there is no interest or position, ask for a referral.

*Example: Follow-up with **Has Not Seen Resume** employer response. Resume Faxed, Followed-up and Yes, There Is an Interest response.*

RMF EMPLOYER CONTACT FORM

Contact Dates:
Date mailed: 1/15/96 Anticipated follow-up date 1/22/96
Actual follow-up date 1/23/96

★ ★ ★ ★ ★

RESEARCH PHASE:
Organization's Name: Pfeifer Corporation
Contact Name/Title: Jacque Quinn, Lab Manager
Address: 127 Skyline Drive
Denver, Co 31767
Telephone Number: (515) 555-5555 Fax Number: (515) 555-5556
Notes: Company referred by Professor Smith and posted on Monster Board of Internet. BioTech firm manufactures antibiotics and other pharmaceuticals. Co. established 1938, Sales in excess of $300 mm. Ms. Quinn an ASU grad, studied under Prof. Smith. Has hired MS. Biochem majors for entry level position in past, according to Dr. Smith.

Build your cover letter based on the research you have conducted. Place your letter along with your resume in the mail and move to the Mail Phase.

★ ★ ★ ★ ★

MAIL PHASE:
For geographically local companies, wait 4 to 6 days and then proceed to the Follow-up Phase.
For geographically distant companies wait 5 to 7 days and then proceed to the Follow-up Phase.
Begin doing research on more companies.

★ ★ ★ ★ ★

FOLLOW-UP PHASE:
Place telephone call to the employer.

1) Introduce yourself
2) Tell purpose of phone call
3) Present 20-second commercial
4) Determine if there is an interest
5) Go to back of contact form and follow appropriate follow-up action.

Messages:
Date/Time: 1/23/96 9:00 am
Date/Time: 1/25/96 1:15 pm
Date/Time: 1/28/96 4:00 pm

Called me back 1/28/96 - 5:00pm

Secretary's name ____________________

★ ★ ★

FOLLOW-UP ACTION:

☒ **Yes, There Is an Interest:**

Build your marketing plan by gathering as much information as you can about the position. Take notes!

Position/title: Biochemist

Position reports to: Jacque Quinn

Skills/experience required:

Is sending detailed Job Description in mail today. stressed a need to get PhD! Call on 2/3/96 to set-up interview and travel/Hotel arrangements.

Interview date/time: ______

Directions:

★ ★ ★

☐ **No Interest or No Position:**

Ask for a referral!

Name of referred company: ______

Name/title of referred employer: ______

Address: ______

Telephone Number: ______

★ ★ ★

☒ **Has Not Seen Resume:**

Geographically local employer — Suggest that you drop off the resume at a specified date and time. If employer says yes, proceed to ☒ **Yes, There Is an Interest** and build your marketing plan and set up an appointment. If employer responds by saying no interest or nothing open, proceed to ☐ **No Interest or No Position** and ask for a referral.

Geographically distant employer — Establish most expeditious method of sending information to employer with follow-up date and time.

Follow-up date/time: 1/29/96 FAX Follow-up 3:00 pm

If there is no interest or position, ask for a referral.

*Example: Follow-up with **Has Not Seen Resume** response and No Interest or No Position. Referral given.*

RMF EMPLOYER CONTACT FORM

Contact Dates:

Date mailed: 1/15/96 Anticipated follow-up date 1/22/96

Actual follow-up date 1/22/96

★ ★ ★ ★ ★

RESEARCH PHASE:

Organization's Name: McDowell Securities

Contact Name/Title: Jim Sperry, Sales Manager

Address: 896 N. 22nd St.

Rockford, IL 60621

Telephone Number: (708) 515-5555 Fax Number: (708) 515-5554

Notes:

Prospected company from Chicago Tribune article. Says one of fastest growing in Midwest. No other info available at time.

Build your cover letter based on the research you have conducted. Place your letter along with your resume in the mail and move to the Mail Phase.

★ ★ ★ ★ ★

MAIL PHASE:

For geographically local companies, wait 4 to 6 days and then proceed to the Follow-up Phase. For geographically distant companies wait 5 to 7 days and then proceed to the Follow-up Phase. Begin doing research on more companies.

★ ★ ★ ★ ★

FOLLOW-UP PHASE:

Place telephone call to the employer.

1) Introduce yourself
2) Tell purpose of phone call
3) Present 20-second commercial
4) Determine if there is an interest
5) Go to back of contact form and follow appropriate follow-up action.

Messages:

Date/Time: 1/22/96 2:30 pm

Date/Time:

Date/Time:

Secretary's name Sandy – said try back at 3:30 Chicago time.

★ ★ ★

FOLLOW-UP ACTION:

☐ **Yes, There Is an Interest:**

Build your marketing plan by gathering as much information as you can about the position. Take notes!

Position/title: ______________________________

Position reports to: ______________________________

Skills/experience required:

Interview date/time: ______________________________

Directions:

★ ★ ★

☒ **No Interest or No Position:**

Ask for a referral!

Name of referred company: Elliot Financial Inc.

Name/title of referred employer: Dick Jones, Sales/mktg Mgr.

Address: Jim Sperry doesn't have address
said to phone and use his name

Telephone Number: (708) 555-3838

★ ★ ★

☒ **Has Not Seen Resume:**

Geographically local employer — Suggest that you drop off the resume at a specified date and time. If employer says yes, proceed to ☐ **Yes, There Is an Interest** and build your marketing plan and set up an appointment. If employer responds by saying no interest or nothing open, proceed to ☒ **No Interest or No Position** and ask for a referral.

Geographically distant employer — Establish most expeditious method of sending information to employer with follow-up date and time.

Follow-up date/time: ______________________________

If there is no interest or position, ask for a referral.

Time to Get Started

Now that you know how to use the system, have your 10 Job Search Goals in place, and can apply your RMF Employer Contact Forms, you're ready to get started. **Begin today!** Don't wait until next week. Your competition has already started to conduct their research. Sometimes the thought of getting started is worse than actually starting. Go to the library or your university's career center and do it. You're in control. You have the knowledge. Don't put this off.

I wish you success in your job search.

60 RMF Employer Contact Forms

RMF Employer Contact Form

Contact Dates:
Date mailed: ______________________ Anticipated follow-up date ______________
Actual follow-up date ________________

★ ★ ★ ★ ★

Research Phase:
Organization's Name: ____
Contact Name/Title: ____
Address: ____
____
Telephone Number: ____________________ Fax Number: ____________________
Notes:

Build your cover letter based on the research you have conducted. Place your letter along with your resume in the mail and move to the Mail Phase.

★ ★ ★ ★ ★

Mail Phase:
For geographically local companies, wait 4 to 6 days and then proceed to the Follow-up Phase.
For geographically distant companies wait 5 to 7 days and then proceed to the Follow-up Phase.
Begin doing research on more companies.

★ ★ ★ ★ ★

Follow-up Phase:
Place telephone call to the employer.

1) Introduce yourself
2) Tell purpose of phone call
3) Present 20-second commercial
4) Determine if there is an interest
5) Go to back of contact form and follow appropriate follow-up action.

Messages:
Date/Time: ____
Date/Time: ____
Date/Time: ____

Secretary's name ____

★ ★ ★

FOLLOW-UP ACTION:

❑ **Yes, There Is an Interest:**

Build your marketing plan by gathering as much information as you can about the position. Take notes!

Position/title: ______________________________

Position reports to: ______________________________

Skills/experience required:

Interview date/time: ______________________________

Directions:

★ ★ ★

❑ **No Interest or No Position:**

Ask for a referral!

Name of referred company: ______________________________

Name/title of referred employer: ______________________________

Address: ______________________________

____

____

Telephone Number: ____________________

★ ★ ★

❑ **Has Not Seen Resume:**

Geographically local employer — Suggest that you drop off the resume at a specified date and time. If employer says yes, proceed to ❑ **Yes, There Is an Interest** and build your marketing plan and set up an appointment. If employer responds by saying no interest or nothing open, proceed to ❑ **No Interest or No Position** and ask for a referral.

Geographically distant employer — Establish most expeditious method of sending information to employer with follow-up date and time.

Follow-up date/time: ____________________

If there is no interest or position, ask for a referral.

RMF Employer Contact Form

Contact Dates:

Date mailed: ______________________ Anticipated follow-up date ______________

Actual follow-up date ________________

★ ★ ★ ★ ★

Research Phase:

Organization's Name: ______________________________________

Contact Name/Title: ______________________________________

Address: ______________________________________

____

Telephone Number: ____________________ Fax Number: ____________________

Notes:

Build your cover letter based on the research you have conducted. Place your letter along with your resume in the mail and move to the Mail Phase.

★ ★ ★ ★ ★

Mail Phase:

For geographically local companies, wait 4 to 6 days and then proceed to the Follow-up Phase. For geographically distant companies wait 5 to 7 days and then proceed to the Follow-up Phase. Begin doing research on more companies.

★ ★ ★ ★ ★

Follow-up Phase:

Place telephone call to the employer.

1) Introduce yourself
2) Tell purpose of phone call
3) Present 20-second commercial
4) Determine if there is an interest
5) Go to back of contact form and follow appropriate follow-up action.

Messages:

Date/Time: ______________________________________

Date/Time: ______________________________________

Date/Time: ______________________________________

Secretary's name ______________________________________

★ ★ ★

FOLLOW-UP ACTION:

❑ **Yes, There Is an Interest:**

Build your marketing plan by gathering as much information as you can about the position. Take notes!

Position/title: ____________________

Position reports to: ____________________

Skills/experience required:

Interview date/time: ____________________

Directions:

★ ★ ★

❑ **No Interest or No Position:**

Ask for a referral!

Name of referred company: ____________________

Name/title of referred employer: ____________________

Address: ____________________

____

____

Telephone Number: ____________________

★ ★ ★

❑ **Has Not Seen Resume:**

Geographically local employer — Suggest that you drop off the resume at a specified date and time. If employer says yes, proceed to ❑ **Yes, There Is an Interest** and build your marketing plan and set up an appointment. If employer responds by saying no interest or nothing open, proceed to ❑ **No Interest or No Position** and ask for a referral.

Geographically distant employer — Establish most expeditious method of sending information to employer with follow-up date and time.

Follow-up date/time: ____________________

If there is no interest or position, ask for a referral.

RMF Employer Contact Form

Contact Dates:
Date mailed: ______________________ Anticipated follow-up date ______________
Actual follow-up date ________________

★ ★ ★ ★ ★

Research Phase:
Organization's Name: ________________________________
Contact Name/Title: ________________________________
Address: ________________________________
____
Telephone Number: ____________________ Fax Number: ____________________
Notes:

Build your cover letter based on the research you have conducted. Place your letter along with your resume in the mail and move to the Mail Phase.

★ ★ ★ ★ ★

Mail Phase:
For geographically local companies, wait 4 to 6 days and then proceed to the Follow-up Phase.
For geographically distant companies wait 5 to 7 days and then proceed to the Follow-up Phase.
Begin doing research on more companies.

★ ★ ★ ★ ★

Follow-up Phase:
Place telephone call to the employer.

1) Introduce yourself
2) Tell purpose of phone call
3) Present 20-second commercial
4) Determine if there is an interest
5) Go to back of contact form and follow appropriate follow-up action.

Messages:
Date/Time: ________________________________
Date/Time: ________________________________
Date/Time: ________________________________

Secretary's name ________________________________

★ ★ ★

FOLLOW-UP ACTION:

❑ **Yes, There Is an Interest:**

Build your marketing plan by gathering as much information as you can about the position. Take notes!

Position/title: ______________________________

Position reports to: ______________________________

Skills/experience required:

Interview date/time: ______________________________

Directions:

★ ★ ★

❑ **No Interest or No Position:**

Ask for a referral!

Name of referred company: ______________________________

Name/title of referred employer: ______________________________

Address: ______________________________

____

____

Telephone Number: ____________________

★ ★ ★

❑ **Has Not Seen Resume:**

Geographically local employer — Suggest that you drop off the resume at a specified date and time. If employer says yes, proceed to ❑ **Yes, There Is an Interest** and build your marketing plan and set up an appointment. If employer responds by saying no interest or nothing open, proceed to ❑ **No Interest or No Position** and ask for a referral.

Geographically distant employer — Establish most expeditious method of sending information to employer with follow-up date and time.

Follow-up date/time: ____________________

If there is no interest or position, ask for a referral.

RMF Employer Contact Form

Contact Dates:

Date mailed: ______________________ Anticipated follow-up date ______________

Actual follow-up date ______________

★ ★ ★ ★ ★

Research Phase:

Organization's Name: ____

Contact Name/Title: ____

Address: ____

____

Telephone Number: ______________________ Fax Number: ______________________

Notes:

Build your cover letter based on the research you have conducted. Place your letter along with your resume in the mail and move to the Mail Phase.

★ ★ ★ ★ ★

Mail Phase:

For geographically local companies, wait 4 to 6 days and then proceed to the Follow-up Phase. For geographically distant companies wait 5 to 7 days and then proceed to the Follow-up Phase. Begin doing research on more companies.

★ ★ ★ ★ ★

Follow-up Phase:

Place telephone call to the employer.

1) Introduce yourself
2) Tell purpose of phone call
3) Present 20-second commercial
4) Determine if there is an interest
5) Go to back of contact form and follow appropriate follow-up action.

Messages:

Date/Time: ____

Date/Time: ____

Date/Time: ____

Secretary's name ____

★ ★ ★

FOLLOW-UP ACTION:

❑ **Yes, There Is an Interest:**

Build your marketing plan by gathering as much information as you can about the position. Take notes!

Position/title: ______________________________

Position reports to: ______________________________

Skills/experience required:

Interview date/time: ______________________________

Directions:

★ ★ ★

❑ **No Interest or No Position:**

Ask for a referral!

Name of referred company: ______________________________

Name/title of referred employer: ______________________________

Address: ______________________________

____

____

Telephone Number: ____________________

★ ★ ★

❑ **Has Not Seen Resume:**

Geographically local employer — Suggest that you drop off the resume at a specified date and time. If employer says yes, proceed to ❑ **Yes, There Is an Interest** and build your marketing plan and set up an appointment. If employer responds by saying no interest or nothing open, proceed to ❑ **No Interest or No Position** and ask for a referral.

Geographically distant employer — Establish most expeditious method of sending information to employer with follow-up date and time.

Follow-up date/time: ____________________

If there is no interest or position, ask for a referral.

RMF Employer Contact Form

Contact Dates:

Date mailed: ______________________ Anticipated follow-up date ______________

Actual follow-up date ________________

★ ★ ★ ★ ★

Research Phase:

Organization's Name: ____

Contact Name/Title: ____

Address: ____

____

Telephone Number: ____________________ Fax Number: ____________________

Notes:

Build your cover letter based on the research you have conducted. Place your letter along with your resume in the mail and move to the Mail Phase.

★ ★ ★ ★ ★

Mail Phase:

For geographically local companies, wait 4 to 6 days and then proceed to the Follow-up Phase. For geographically distant companies wait 5 to 7 days and then proceed to the Follow-up Phase. Begin doing research on more companies.

★ ★ ★ ★ ★

Follow-up Phase:

Place telephone call to the employer.

1) Introduce yourself
2) Tell purpose of phone call
3) Present 20-second commercial
4) Determine if there is an interest
5) Go to back of contact form and follow appropriate follow-up action.

Messages:

Date/Time: ____

Date/Time: ____

Date/Time: ____

Secretary's name ____

★ ★ ★

FOLLOW-UP ACTION:

❑ **Yes, There Is an Interest:**

Build your marketing plan by gathering as much information as you can about the position. Take notes!

Position/title: ______________________________

Position reports to: ______________________________

Skills/experience required:

Interview date/time: ______________________________

Directions:

★ ★ ★

❑ **No Interest or No Position:**

Ask for a referral!

Name of referred company: ______________________________

Name/title of referred employer: ______________________________

Address: ______________________________

____

____

Telephone Number: ____________________

★ ★ ★

❑ **Has Not Seen Resume:**

Geographically local employer — Suggest that you drop off the resume at a specified date and time. If employer says yes, proceed to ❑ **Yes, There Is an Interest** and build your marketing plan and set up an appointment. If employer responds by saying no interest or nothing open, proceed to ❑ **No Interest or No Position** and ask for a referral.

Geographically distant employer — Establish most expeditious method of sending information to employer with follow-up date and time.

Follow-up date/time: ____________________

If there is no interest or position, ask for a referral.

RMF Employer Contact Form

Contact Dates:

Date mailed: ______________________ Anticipated follow-up date ______________

Actual follow-up date ________________

★ ★ ★ ★ ★

Research Phase:

Organization's Name: ____

Contact Name/Title: ____

Address: ____

____

Telephone Number: ______________________ Fax Number: ______________________

Notes:

Build your cover letter based on the research you have conducted. Place your letter along with your resume in the mail and move to the Mail Phase.

★ ★ ★ ★ ★

Mail Phase:

For geographically local companies, wait 4 to 6 days and then proceed to the Follow-up Phase. For geographically distant companies wait 5 to 7 days and then proceed to the Follow-up Phase. Begin doing research on more companies.

★ ★ ★ ★ ★

Follow-up Phase:

Place telephone call to the employer.

1) Introduce yourself
2) Tell purpose of phone call
3) Present 20-second commercial
4) Determine if there is an interest
5) Go to back of contact form and follow appropriate follow-up action.

Messages:

Date/Time: ____

Date/Time: ____

Date/Time: ____

Secretary's name ____

★ ★ ★

FOLLOW-UP ACTION:

❑ **Yes, There Is an Interest:**

Build your marketing plan by gathering as much information as you can about the position. Take notes!

Position/title: ____________________

Position reports to: ____________________

Skills/experience required:

Interview date/time: ____________________

Directions:

★ ★ ★

❑ **No Interest or No Position:**

Ask for a referral!

Name of referred company: ____________________

Name/title of referred employer: ____________________

Address: ____________________

____

____

Telephone Number: ____________________

★ ★ ★

❑ **Has Not Seen Resume:**

Geographically local employer — Suggest that you drop off the resume at a specified date and time. If employer says yes, proceed to ❑ **Yes, There Is an Interest** and build your marketing plan and set up an appointment. If employer responds by saying no interest or nothing open, proceed to ❑ **No Interest or No Position** and ask for a referral.

Geographically distant employer — Establish most expeditious method of sending information to employer with follow-up date and time.

Follow-up date/time: ____________________

If there is no interest or position, ask for a referral.

RMF Employer Contact Form

Contact Dates:
Date mailed: ______________________ Anticipated follow-up date ______________
Actual follow-up date ______________

★ ★ ★ ★ ★

Research Phase:
Organization's Name: ______________________________
Contact Name/Title: ______________________________
Address: ______________________________
____
Telephone Number: ______________________ Fax Number: ______________________
Notes:

Build your cover letter based on the research you have conducted. Place your letter along with your resume in the mail and move to the Mail Phase.

★ ★ ★ ★ ★

Mail Phase:
For geographically local companies, wait 4 to 6 days and then proceed to the Follow-up Phase.
For geographically distant companies wait 5 to 7 days and then proceed to the Follow-up Phase.
Begin doing research on more companies.

★ ★ ★ ★ ★

Follow-up Phase:
Place telephone call to the employer.

1) Introduce yourself
2) Tell purpose of phone call
3) Present 20-second commercial
4) Determine if there is an interest
5) Go to back of contact form and follow appropriate follow-up action.

Messages:
Date/Time: ______________________________
Date/Time: ______________________________
Date/Time: ______________________________

Secretary's name ______________________________

★ ★ ★

Follow-up Action:

❑ **Yes, There Is an Interest:**

Build your marketing plan by gathering as much information as you can about the position. Take notes!

Position/title: ______________________________

Position reports to: ______________________________

Skills/experience required:

Interview date/time: ______________________________

Directions:

★ ★ ★

❑ **No Interest or No Position:**

Ask for a referral!

Name of referred company: ______________________________

Name/title of referred employer: ______________________________

Address: ______________________________

____

____

Telephone Number: ______________________________

★ ★ ★

❑ **Has Not Seen Resume:**

Geographically local employer — Suggest that you drop off the resume at a specified date and time. If employer says yes, proceed to ❑ **Yes, There Is an Interest** and build your marketing plan and set up an appointment. If employer responds by saying no interest or nothing open, proceed to ❑ **No Interest or No Position** and ask for a referral.

Geographically distant employer — Establish most expeditious method of sending information to employer with follow-up date and time.

Follow-up date/time: ______________________________

If there is no interest or position, ask for a referral.

RMF Employer Contact Form

Contact Dates:
Date mailed: ______________________ Anticipated follow-up date ______________
Actual follow-up date ________________

★ ★ ★ ★ ★

Research Phase:
Organization's Name: ____
Contact Name/Title: ____
Address: ____
____
Telephone Number: ____________________ Fax Number: ____________________
Notes:

Build your cover letter based on the research you have conducted. Place your letter along with your resume in the mail and move to the Mail Phase.

★ ★ ★ ★ ★

Mail Phase:
For geographically local companies, wait 4 to 6 days and then proceed to the Follow-up Phase.
For geographically distant companies wait 5 to 7 days and then proceed to the Follow-up Phase.
Begin doing research on more companies.

★ ★ ★ ★ ★

Follow-up Phase:
Place telephone call to the employer.

1) Introduce yourself
2) Tell purpose of phone call
3) Present 20-second commercial
4) Determine if there is an interest
5) Go to back of contact form and follow appropriate follow-up action.

Messages:
Date/Time: ____
Date/Time: ____
Date/Time: ____

Secretary's name ____

★ ★ ★

FOLLOW-UP ACTION:

❑ **Yes, There Is an Interest:**

Build your marketing plan by gathering as much information as you can about the position. Take notes!

Position/title: ______________________________

Position reports to: ______________________________

Skills/experience required:

Interview date/time: ______________________________

Directions:

★ ★ ★

❑ **No Interest or No Position:**

Ask for a referral!

Name of referred company: ______________________________

Name/title of referred employer: ______________________________

Address: ______________________________

____

____

Telephone Number: ____________________

★ ★ ★

❑ **Has Not Seen Resume:**

Geographically local employer — Suggest that you drop off the resume at a specified date and time. If employer says yes, proceed to ❑ **Yes, There Is an Interest** and build your marketing plan and set up an appointment. If employer responds by saying no interest or nothing open, proceed to ❑ **No Interest or No Position** and ask for a referral.

Geographically distant employer — Establish most expeditious method of sending information to employer with follow-up date and time.

Follow-up date/time: ____________________

If there is no interest or position, ask for a referral.

RMF Employer Contact Form

Contact Dates:

Date mailed: ______________________________ Anticipated follow-up date ________________

Actual follow-up date ______________________

★ ★ ★ ★ ★

Research Phase:

Organization's Name: ____

Contact Name/Title: ____

Address: ____

____

Telephone Number: ________________________ Fax Number: ________________________

Notes:

Build your cover letter based on the research you have conducted. Place your letter along with your resume in the mail and move to the Mail Phase.

★ ★ ★ ★ ★

Mail Phase:

For geographically local companies, wait 4 to 6 days and then proceed to the Follow-up Phase. For geographically distant companies wait 5 to 7 days and then proceed to the Follow-up Phase. Begin doing research on more companies.

★ ★ ★ ★ ★

Follow-up Phase:

Place telephone call to the employer.

1) Introduce yourself
2) Tell purpose of phone call
3) Present 20-second commercial
4) Determine if there is an interest
5) Go to back of contact form and follow appropriate follow-up action.

Messages:

Date/Time: ____

Date/Time: ____

Date/Time: ____

Secretary's name ____

★ ★ ★

FOLLOW-UP ACTION:

❑ **Yes, There Is an Interest:**

Build your marketing plan by gathering as much information as you can about the position. Take notes!

Position/title: ____________________

Position reports to: ____________________

Skills/experience required:

Interview date/time: ____________________

Directions:

★ ★ ★

❑ **No Interest or No Position:**

Ask for a referral!

Name of referred company: ____________________

Name/title of referred employer: ____________________

Address: ____________________

____

____

Telephone Number: ____________________

★ ★ ★

❑ **Has Not Seen Resume:**

Geographically local employer — Suggest that you drop off the resume at a specified date and time. If employer says yes, proceed to ❑ **Yes, There Is an Interest** and build your marketing plan and set up an appointment. If employer responds by saying no interest or nothing open, proceed to ❑ **No Interest or No Position** and ask for a referral.

Geographically distant employer — Establish most expeditious method of sending information to employer with follow-up date and time.

Follow-up date/time: ____________________

If there is no interest or position, ask for a referral.

RMF Employer Contact Form

Contact Dates:
Date mailed: ______________________ Anticipated follow-up date ______________
Actual follow-up date ________________

★ ★ ★ ★ ★

Research Phase:
Organization's Name: ______________________________________
Contact Name/Title: ______________________________________
Address: ______________________________________
____
Telephone Number: ______________________ Fax Number: ____________________
Notes:

Build your cover letter based on the research you have conducted. Place your letter along with your resume in the mail and move to the Mail Phase.

★ ★ ★ ★ ★

Mail Phase:
For geographically local companies, wait 4 to 6 days and then proceed to the Follow-up Phase.
For geographically distant companies wait 5 to 7 days and then proceed to the Follow-up Phase.
Begin doing research on more companies.

★ ★ ★ ★ ★

Follow-up Phase:
Place telephone call to the employer.

1) Introduce yourself
2) Tell purpose of phone call
3) Present 20-second commercial
4) Determine if there is an interest
5) Go to back of contact form and follow appropriate follow-up action.

Messages:
Date/Time: ______________________________________
Date/Time: ______________________________________
Date/Time: ______________________________________

Secretary's name ______________________________________

★ ★ ★

Follow-up Action:

❑ **Yes, There Is an Interest:**

Build your marketing plan by gathering as much information as you can about the position. Take notes!

Position/title: ____________________

Position reports to: ____________________

Skills/experience required:

Interview date/time: ____________________

Directions:

★ ★ ★

❑ **No Interest or No Position:**

Ask for a referral!

Name of referred company: ____________________

Name/title of referred employer: ____________________

Address: ____________________

____

____

Telephone Number: ____________________

★ ★ ★

❑ **Has Not Seen Resume:**

Geographically local employer — Suggest that you drop off the resume at a specified date and time. If employer says yes, proceed to ❑ **Yes, There Is an Interest** and build your marketing plan and set up an appointment. If employer responds by saying no interest or nothing open, proceed to ❑ **No Interest or No Position** and ask for a referral.

Geographically distant employer — Establish most expeditious method of sending information to employer with follow-up date and time.

Follow-up date/time: ____________________

If there is no interest or position, ask for a referral.

RMF Employer Contact Form

Contact Dates:
Date mailed: ______________________ Anticipated follow-up date ______________
Actual follow-up date ________________

★ ★ ★ ★ ★

Research Phase:
Organization's Name: ______________________________
Contact Name/Title: ______________________________
Address: ______________________________
____
Telephone Number: ____________________ Fax Number: ____________________
Notes:

Build your cover letter based on the research you have conducted. Place your letter along with your resume in the mail and move to the Mail Phase.

★ ★ ★ ★ ★

Mail Phase:
For geographically local companies, wait 4 to 6 days and then proceed to the Follow-up Phase.
For geographically distant companies wait 5 to 7 days and then proceed to the Follow-up Phase.
Begin doing research on more companies.

★ ★ ★ ★ ★

Follow-up Phase:
Place telephone call to the employer.

1) Introduce yourself
2) Tell purpose of phone call
3) Present 20-second commercial
4) Determine if there is an interest
5) Go to back of contact form and follow appropriate follow-up action.

Messages:
Date/Time: ______________________________
Date/Time: ______________________________
Date/Time: ______________________________

Secretary's name ______________________________

★ ★ ★

FOLLOW-UP ACTION:

❑ **Yes, There Is an Interest:**

Build your marketing plan by gathering as much information as you can about the position. Take notes!

Position/title: ______________________________

Position reports to: ______________________________

Skills/experience required:

Interview date/time: ______________________________

Directions:

★ ★ ★

❑ **No Interest or No Position:**

Ask for a referral!

Name of referred company: ______________________________

Name/title of referred employer: ______________________________

Address: ______________________________

____

____

Telephone Number: ____________________

★ ★ ★

❑ **Has Not Seen Resume:**

Geographically local employer — Suggest that you drop off the resume at a specified date and time. If employer says yes, proceed to ❑ **Yes, There Is an Interest** and build your marketing plan and set up an appointment. If employer responds by saying no interest or nothing open, proceed to ❑ **No Interest or No Position** and ask for a referral.

Geographically distant employer — Establish most expeditious method of sending information to employer with follow-up date and time.

Follow-up date/time: ____________________

If there is no interest or position, ask for a referral.

RMF Employer Contact Form

Contact Dates:
Date mailed: ______________________________ Anticipated follow-up date __________________
Actual follow-up date ______________________

★ ★ ★ ★ ★

Research Phase:
Organization's Name: ____
Contact Name/Title: ____
Address: ____
____
Telephone Number: ____________________________ Fax Number: ___________________________
Notes:

Build your cover letter based on the research you have conducted. Place your letter along with your resume in the mail and move to the Mail Phase.

★ ★ ★ ★ ★

Mail Phase:
For geographically local companies, wait 4 to 6 days and then proceed to the Follow-up Phase. For geographically distant companies wait 5 to 7 days and then proceed to the Follow-up Phase. Begin doing research on more companies.

★ ★ ★ ★ ★

Follow-up Phase:
Place telephone call to the employer.

1) Introduce yourself
2) Tell purpose of phone call
3) Present 20-second commercial
4) Determine if there is an interest
5) Go to back of contact form and follow appropriate follow-up action.

Messages:
Date/Time: ____
Date/Time: ____
Date/Time: ____

Secretary's name ____

★ ★ ★

Follow-up Action:

❑ **Yes, There Is an Interest:**

Build your marketing plan by gathering as much information as you can about the position. Take notes!

Position/title: ______________________________

Position reports to: ______________________________

Skills/experience required:

Interview date/time: ______________________________

Directions:

★ ★ ★

❑ **No Interest or No Position:**

Ask for a referral!

Name of referred company: ______________________________

Name/title of referred employer: ______________________________

Address: ______________________________
____
____

Telephone Number: ____________________

★ ★ ★

❑ **Has Not Seen Resume:**

Geographically local employer — Suggest that you drop off the resume at a specified date and time. If employer says yes, proceed to ❑ **Yes, There Is an Interest** and build your marketing plan and set up an appointment. If employer responds by saying no interest or nothing open, proceed to ❑ **No Interest or No Position** and ask for a referral.

Geographically distant employer — Establish most expeditious method of sending information to employer with follow-up date and time.

Follow-up date/time: ____________________

If there is no interest or position, ask for a referral.

RMF Employer Contact Form

Contact Dates:
Date mailed: ____________________ Anticipated follow-up date ____________
Actual follow-up date ____________

★ ★ ★ ★ ★

Research Phase:
Organization's Name: ______________________________
Contact Name/Title: ______________________________
Address: ______________________________
____
Telephone Number: ____________________ Fax Number: ____________________
Notes:

Build your cover letter based on the research you have conducted. Place your letter along with your resume in the mail and move to the Mail Phase.

★ ★ ★ ★ ★

Mail Phase:
For geographically local companies, wait 4 to 6 days and then proceed to the Follow-up Phase.
For geographically distant companies wait 5 to 7 days and then proceed to the Follow-up Phase.
Begin doing research on more companies.

★ ★ ★ ★ ★

Follow-up Phase:
Place telephone call to the employer.

1) Introduce yourself
2) Tell purpose of phone call
3) Present 20-second commercial
4) Determine if there is an interest
5) Go to back of contact form and follow appropriate follow-up action.

Messages:
Date/Time: ______________________________
Date/Time: ______________________________
Date/Time: ______________________________

Secretary's name ______________________________

★ ★ ★

FOLLOW-UP ACTION:

❑ **Yes, There Is an Interest:**

Build your marketing plan by gathering as much information as you can about the position. Take notes!

Position/title: ______________________________

Position reports to: ______________________________

Skills/experience required:

Interview date/time: ______________________________

Directions:

★ ★ ★

❑ **No Interest or No Position:**

Ask for a referral!

Name of referred company: ______________________________

Name/title of referred employer: ______________________________

Address: ______________________________

____

____

Telephone Number: ______________________

★ ★ ★

❑ **Has Not Seen Resume:**

Geographically local employer — Suggest that you drop off the resume at a specified date and time. If employer says yes, proceed to ❑ **Yes, There Is an Interest** and build your marketing plan and set up an appointment. If employer responds by saying no interest or nothing open, proceed to ❑ **No Interest or No Position** and ask for a referral.

Geographically distant employer — Establish most expeditious method of sending information to employer with follow-up date and time.

Follow-up date/time: ____________________

If there is no interest or position, ask for a referral.

RMF Employer Contact Form

Contact Dates:
Date mailed: ____________________ Anticipated follow-up date ______________
Actual follow-up date ______________

★ ★ ★ ★ ★

Research Phase:
Organization's Name: ________________________________
Contact Name/Title: ________________________________
Address: ________________________________
____
Telephone Number: ____________________ Fax Number: ____________________
Notes:

Build your cover letter based on the research you have conducted. Place your letter along with your resume in the mail and move to the Mail Phase.

★ ★ ★ ★ ★

Mail Phase:
For geographically local companies, wait 4 to 6 days and then proceed to the Follow-up Phase.
For geographically distant companies wait 5 to 7 days and then proceed to the Follow-up Phase.
Begin doing research on more companies.

★ ★ ★ ★ ★

Follow-up Phase:
Place telephone call to the employer.

1) Introduce yourself
2) Tell purpose of phone call
3) Present 20-second commercial
4) Determine if there is an interest
5) Go to back of contact form and follow appropriate follow-up action.

Messages:
Date/Time: ________________________________
Date/Time: ________________________________
Date/Time: ________________________________

Secretary's name ________________________________

★ ★ ★

Follow-up Action:

❑ **Yes, There Is an Interest:**

Build your marketing plan by gathering as much information as you can about the position. Take notes!

Position/title: ______________________________

Position reports to: ______________________________

Skills/experience required:

Interview date/time: ______________________________

Directions:

★ ★ ★

❑ **No Interest or No Position:**

Ask for a referral!

Name of referred company: ______________________________

Name/title of referred employer: ______________________________

Address: ______________________________

____

____

Telephone Number: ____________________

★ ★ ★

❑ **Has Not Seen Resume:**

Geographically local employer — Suggest that you drop off the resume at a specified date and time. If employer says yes, proceed to ❑ **Yes, There Is an Interest** and build your marketing plan and set up an appointment. If employer responds by saying no interest or nothing open, proceed to ❑ **No Interest or No Position** and ask for a referral.

Geographically distant employer — Establish most expeditious method of sending information to employer with follow-up date and time.

Follow-up date/time: ____________________

If there is no interest or position, ask for a referral.

RMF Employer Contact Form

Contact Dates:

Date mailed: ______________________ Anticipated follow-up date ______________

Actual follow-up date ________________

★ ★ ★ ★ ★

Research Phase:

Organization's Name: ____

Contact Name/Title: ____

Address: ____

____

Telephone Number: ______________________ Fax Number: ____________________

Notes:

Build your cover letter based on the research you have conducted. Place your letter along with your resume in the mail and move to the Mail Phase.

★ ★ ★ ★ ★

Mail Phase:

For geographically local companies, wait 4 to 6 days and then proceed to the Follow-up Phase.
For geographically distant companies wait 5 to 7 days and then proceed to the Follow-up Phase.
Begin doing research on more companies.

★ ★ ★ ★ ★

Follow-up Phase:

Place telephone call to the employer.

1) Introduce yourself
2) Tell purpose of phone call
3) Present 20-second commercial
4) Determine if there is an interest
5) Go to back of contact form and follow appropriate follow-up action.

Messages:

Date/Time: ____

Date/Time: ____

Date/Time: ____

Secretary's name ____

★ ★ ★

FOLLOW-UP ACTION:

❑ **Yes, There Is an Interest:**

Build your marketing plan by gathering as much information as you can about the position. Take notes!

Position/title: ____________________

Position reports to: ____________________

Skills/experience required:

Interview date/time: ____________________

Directions:

★ ★ ★

❑ **No Interest or No Position:**

Ask for a referral!

Name of referred company: ____________________

Name/title of referred employer: ____________________

Address: ____________________

____

____

Telephone Number: ____________________

★ ★ ★

❑ **Has Not Seen Resume:**

Geographically local employer — Suggest that you drop off the resume at a specified date and time. If employer says yes, proceed to ❑ **Yes, There Is an Interest** and build your marketing plan and set up an appointment. If employer responds by saying no interest or nothing open, proceed to ❑ **No Interest or No Position** and ask for a referral.

Geographically distant employer — Establish most expeditious method of sending information to employer with follow-up date and time.

Follow-up date/time: ____________________

If there is no interest or position, ask for a referral.

RMF Employer Contact Form

Contact Dates:

Date mailed: ______________________ Anticipated follow-up date ______________

Actual follow-up date ______________

★ ★ ★ ★ ★

Research Phase:

Organization's Name: ____

Contact Name/Title: ____

Address: ____

____

Telephone Number: ______________________ Fax Number: ______________________

Notes:

Build your cover letter based on the research you have conducted. Place your letter along with your resume in the mail and move to the Mail Phase.

★ ★ ★ ★ ★

Mail Phase:

For geographically local companies, wait 4 to 6 days and then proceed to the Follow-up Phase. For geographically distant companies wait 5 to 7 days and then proceed to the Follow-up Phase. Begin doing research on more companies.

★ ★ ★ ★ ★

Follow-up Phase:

Place telephone call to the employer.

1) Introduce yourself
2) Tell purpose of phone call
3) Present 20-second commercial
4) Determine if there is an interest
5) Go to back of contact form and follow appropriate follow-up action.

Messages:

Date/Time: ____

Date/Time: ____

Date/Time: ____

Secretary's name ____

★ ★ ★

FOLLOW-UP ACTION:

❑ **Yes, There Is an Interest:**

Build your marketing plan by gathering as much information as you can about the position. Take notes!

Position/title: ______________________________

Position reports to: ______________________________

Skills/experience required:

Interview date/time: ______________________________

Directions:

★ ★ ★

❑ **No Interest or No Position:**

Ask for a referral!

Name of referred company: ______________________________

Name/title of referred employer: ______________________________

Address: ______________________________

____

____

Telephone Number: ____________________

★ ★ ★

❑ **Has Not Seen Resume:**

Geographically local employer — Suggest that you drop off the resume at a specified date and time. If employer says yes, proceed to ❑ **Yes, There Is an Interest** and build your marketing plan and set up an appointment. If employer responds by saying no interest or nothing open, proceed to ❑ **No Interest or No Position** and ask for a referral.

Geographically distant employer — Establish most expeditious method of sending information to employer with follow-up date and time.

Follow-up date/time: ____________________

If there is no interest or position, ask for a referral.

RMF EMPLOYER CONTACT FORM

Contact Dates:
Date mailed: ______________________ Anticipated follow-up date ______________
Actual follow-up date ______________

★ ★ ★ ★ ★

RESEARCH PHASE:
Organization's Name: ______________________________
Contact Name/Title: ______________________________
Address: ______________________________
____
Telephone Number: ______________________ Fax Number: ______________________
Notes:

Build your cover letter based on the research you have conducted. Place your letter along with your resume in the mail and move to the Mail Phase.

★ ★ ★ ★ ★

MAIL PHASE:
For geographically local companies, wait 4 to 6 days and then proceed to the Follow-up Phase. For geographically distant companies wait 5 to 7 days and then proceed to the Follow-up Phase. Begin doing research on more companies.

★ ★ ★ ★ ★

FOLLOW-UP PHASE:
Place telephone call to the employer.

1) Introduce yourself
2) Tell purpose of phone call
3) Present 20-second commercial
4) Determine if there is an interest
5) Go to back of contact form and follow appropriate follow-up action.

Messages:
Date/Time: ______________________________
Date/Time: ______________________________
Date/Time: ______________________________

Secretary's name ______________________________

★ ★ ★

FOLLOW-UP ACTION:

❑ **Yes, There Is an Interest:**

Build your marketing plan by gathering as much information as you can about the position. Take notes!

Position/title: ______________________________

Position reports to: ______________________________

Skills/experience required:

Interview date/time: ______________________________

Directions:

★ ★ ★

❑ **No Interest or No Position:**

Ask for a referral!

Name of referred company: ______________________________

Name/title of referred employer: ______________________________

Address: ______________________________

____

____

Telephone Number: ____________________

★ ★ ★

❑ **Has Not Seen Resume:**

Geographically local employer — Suggest that you drop off the resume at a specified date and time. If employer says yes, proceed to ❑ **Yes, There Is an Interest** and build your marketing plan and set up an appointment. If employer responds by saying no interest or nothing open, proceed to ❑ **No Interest or No Position** and ask for a referral.

Geographically distant employer — Establish most expeditious method of sending information to employer with follow-up date and time.

Follow-up date/time: ____________________

If there is no interest or position, ask for a referral.

RMF Employer Contact Form

Contact Dates:
Date mailed: ______________________ Anticipated follow-up date ______________
Actual follow-up date ________________

★ ★ ★ ★ ★

Research Phase:
Organization's Name: ____
Contact Name/Title: ____
Address: ____
____
Telephone Number: ____________________ Fax Number: ____________________
Notes:

Build your cover letter based on the research you have conducted. Place your letter along with your resume in the mail and move to the Mail Phase.

★ ★ ★ ★ ★

Mail Phase:
For geographically local companies, wait 4 to 6 days and then proceed to the Follow-up Phase.
For geographically distant companies wait 5 to 7 days and then proceed to the Follow-up Phase.
Begin doing research on more companies.

★ ★ ★ ★ ★

Follow-up Phase:
Place telephone call to the employer.

1) Introduce yourself
2) Tell purpose of phone call
3) Present 20-second commercial
4) Determine if there is an interest
5) Go to back of contact form and follow appropriate follow-up action.

Messages:
Date/Time: ____
Date/Time: ____
Date/Time: ____

Secretary's name ____

★ ★ ★

FOLLOW-UP ACTION:

❑ **Yes, There Is an Interest:**

Build your marketing plan by gathering as much information as you can about the position. Take notes!

Position/title: ______________________________

Position reports to: ______________________________

Skills/experience required:

Interview date/time: ______________________________

Directions:

★ ★ ★

❑ **No Interest or No Position:**

Ask for a referral!

Name of referred company: ______________________________

Name/title of referred employer: ______________________________

Address: ______________________________

____

____

Telephone Number: ____________________

★ ★ ★

❑ **Has Not Seen Resume:**

Geographically local employer — Suggest that you drop off the resume at a specified date and time. If employer says yes, proceed to ❑ **Yes, There Is an Interest** and build your marketing plan and set up an appointment. If employer responds by saying no interest or nothing open, proceed to ❑ **No Interest or No Position** and ask for a referral.

Geographically distant employer — Establish most expeditious method of sending information to employer with follow-up date and time.

Follow-up date/time: ____________________

If there is no interest or position, ask for a referral.

RMF Employer Contact Form

Contact Dates:
Date mailed: ____________________ Anticipated follow-up date ____________
Actual follow-up date ________________

☆ ☆ ☆ ☆ ☆

Research Phase:
Organization's Name: ____________________________________
Contact Name/Title: ____________________________________
Address: ____________________________________
____
Telephone Number: ____________________ Fax Number: ____________________
Notes:

Build your cover letter based on the research you have conducted. Place your letter along with your resume in the mail and move to the Mail Phase.

☆ ☆ ☆ ☆ ☆

Mail Phase:
For geographically local companies, wait 4 to 6 days and then proceed to the Follow-up Phase. For geographically distant companies wait 5 to 7 days and then proceed to the Follow-up Phase. Begin doing research on more companies.

☆ ☆ ☆ ☆ ☆

Follow-up Phase:
Place telephone call to the employer.

1) Introduce yourself
2) Tell purpose of phone call
3) Present 20-second commercial
4) Determine if there is an interest
5) Go to back of contact form and follow appropriate follow-up action.

Messages:
Date/Time: ____________________________________
Date/Time: ____________________________________
Date/Time: ____________________________________

Secretary's name ____________________________________

★ ★ ★

FOLLOW-UP ACTION:

❑ **Yes, There Is an Interest:**

Build your marketing plan by gathering as much information as you can about the position. Take notes!

Position/title: ______________________________

Position reports to: ______________________________

Skills/experience required:

Interview date/time: ______________________________

Directions:

★ ★ ★

❑ **No Interest or No Position:**

Ask for a referral!

Name of referred company: ______________________________

Name/title of referred employer: ______________________________

Address: ______________________________

____

____

Telephone Number: ____________________

★ ★ ★

❑ **Has Not Seen Resume:**

Geographically local employer — Suggest that you drop off the resume at a specified date and time. If employer says yes, proceed to ❑ **Yes, There Is an Interest** and build your marketing plan and set up an appointment. If employer responds by saying no interest or nothing open, proceed to ❑ **No Interest or No Position** and ask for a referral.

Geographically distant employer — Establish most expeditious method of sending information to employer with follow-up date and time.

Follow-up date/time: ____________________

If there is no interest or position, ask for a referral.

RMF Employer Contact Form

Contact Dates:

Date mailed: ______________________ Anticipated follow-up date ______________

Actual follow-up date ______________

★ ★ ★ ★ ★

Research Phase:

Organization's Name: ______________________________

Contact Name/Title: ______________________________

Address: ______________________________

____

Telephone Number: ______________ Fax Number: ______________

Notes:

Build your cover letter based on the research you have conducted. Place your letter along with your resume in the mail and move to the Mail Phase.

★ ★ ★ ★ ★

Mail Phase:

For geographically local companies, wait 4 to 6 days and then proceed to the Follow-up Phase.
For geographically distant companies wait 5 to 7 days and then proceed to the Follow-up Phase.
Begin doing research on more companies.

★ ★ ★ ★ ★

Follow-up Phase:

Place telephone call to the employer.

1) Introduce yourself
2) Tell purpose of phone call
3) Present 20-second commercial
4) Determine if there is an interest
5) Go to back of contact form and follow appropriate follow-up action.

Messages:

Date/Time: ______________________________

Date/Time: ______________________________

Date/Time: ______________________________

Secretary's name ______________________________

★ ★ ★

Follow-up Action:

❑ **Yes, There Is an Interest:**

Build your marketing plan by gathering as much information as you can about the position. Take notes!

Position/title: ____________________

Position reports to: ____________________

Skills/experience required:

Interview date/time: ____________________

Directions:

★ ★ ★

❑ **No Interest or No Position:**

Ask for a referral!

Name of referred company: ____________________

Name/title of referred employer: ____________________

Address: ____________________

____

____

Telephone Number: ____________________

★ ★ ★

❑ **Has Not Seen Resume:**

Geographically local employer — Suggest that you drop off the resume at a specified date and time. If employer says yes, proceed to ❑ **Yes, There Is an Interest** and build your marketing plan and set up an appointment. If employer responds by saying no interest or nothing open, proceed to ❑ **No Interest or No Position** and ask for a referral.

Geographically distant employer — Establish most expeditious method of sending information to employer with follow-up date and time.

Follow-up date/time: ____________________

If there is no interest or position, ask for a referral.

RMF Employer Contact Form

Contact Dates:
Date mailed: ______________________________ Anticipated follow-up date ________________
Actual follow-up date ____________________

★ ★ ★ ★ ★

Research Phase:

Organization's Name: ____

Contact Name/Title: ____

Address: ____

____

Telephone Number: ________________________ Fax Number: ____________________

Notes:

Build your cover letter based on the research you have conducted. Place your letter along with your resume in the mail and move to the Mail Phase.

★ ★ ★ ★ ★

Mail Phase:

For geographically local companies, wait 4 to 6 days and then proceed to the Follow-up Phase. For geographically distant companies wait 5 to 7 days and then proceed to the Follow-up Phase. Begin doing research on more companies.

★ ★ ★ ★ ★

Follow-up Phase:

Place telephone call to the employer.

1) Introduce yourself
2) Tell purpose of phone call
3) Present 20-second commercial
4) Determine if there is an interest
5) Go to back of contact form and follow appropriate follow-up action.

Messages:
Date/Time: ____
Date/Time: ____
Date/Time: ____

Secretary's name ____

★ ★ ★

Follow-up Action:

❑ **Yes, There Is an Interest:**

Build your marketing plan by gathering as much information as you can about the position. Take notes!

Position/title: ______________________________

Position reports to: ______________________________

Skills/experience required:

Interview date/time: ______________________________

Directions:

★ ★ ★

❑ **No Interest or No Position:**

Ask for a referral!

Name of referred company: ______________________________

Name/title of referred employer: ______________________________

Address: ______________________________

____

____

Telephone Number: ____________________

★ ★ ★

❑ **Has Not Seen Resume:**

Geographically local employer — Suggest that you drop off the resume at a specified date and time. If employer says yes, proceed to ❑ **Yes, There Is an Interest** and build your marketing plan and set up an appointment. If employer responds by saying no interest or nothing open, proceed to ❑ **No Interest or No Position** and ask for a referral.

Geographically distant employer — Establish most expeditious method of sending information to employer with follow-up date and time.

Follow-up date/time: ____________________

If there is no interest or position, ask for a referral.

RMF Employer Contact Form

Contact Dates:
Date mailed: ______________________ Anticipated follow-up date ______________
Actual follow-up date __________________

★ ★ ★ ★ ★

Research Phase:
Organization's Name: ____
Contact Name/Title: ____
Address: ____
____
Telephone Number: ______________________ Fax Number: ____________________
Notes:

Build your cover letter based on the research you have conducted. Place your letter along with your resume in the mail and move to the Mail Phase.

★ ★ ★ ★ ★

Mail Phase:
For geographically local companies, wait 4 to 6 days and then proceed to the Follow-up Phase.
For geographically distant companies wait 5 to 7 days and then proceed to the Follow-up Phase.
Begin doing research on more companies.

★ ★ ★ ★ ★

Follow-up Phase:
Place telephone call to the employer.

1) Introduce yourself
2) Tell purpose of phone call
3) Present 20-second commercial
4) Determine if there is an interest
5) Go to back of contact form and follow appropriate follow-up action.

Messages:
Date/Time: ____
Date/Time: ____
Date/Time: ____

Secretary's name ____

★ ★ ★

Follow-up Action:

❑ **Yes, There Is an Interest:**

Build your marketing plan by gathering as much information as you can about the position. Take notes!

Position/title: ______________________________

Position reports to: ______________________________

Skills/experience required:

Interview date/time: ______________________________

Directions:

★ ★ ★

❑ **No Interest or No Position:**

Ask for a referral!

Name of referred company: ______________________________

Name/title of referred employer: ______________________________

Address: ______________________________

____

____

Telephone Number: ____________________

★ ★ ★

❑ **Has Not Seen Resume:**

Geographically local employer — Suggest that you drop off the resume at a specified date and time. If employer says yes, proceed to ❑ **Yes, There Is an Interest** and build your marketing plan and set up an appointment. If employer responds by saying no interest or nothing open, proceed to ❑ **No Interest or No Position** and ask for a referral.

Geographically distant employer — Establish most expeditious method of sending information to employer with follow-up date and time.

Follow-up date/time: ____________________

If there is no interest or position, ask for a referral.

RMF Employer Contact Form

Contact Dates:
Date mailed: ______________________ Anticipated follow-up date ______________
Actual follow-up date ______________

★ ★ ★ ★ ★

Research Phase:
Organization's Name: ______________________________
Contact Name/Title: ______________________________
Address: ______________________________
____
Telephone Number: ______________________ Fax Number: ______________________
Notes:

Build your cover letter based on the research you have conducted. Place your letter along with your resume in the mail and move to the Mail Phase.

★ ★ ★ ★ ★

Mail Phase:
For geographically local companies, wait 4 to 6 days and then proceed to the Follow-up Phase.
For geographically distant companies wait 5 to 7 days and then proceed to the Follow-up Phase.
Begin doing research on more companies.

★ ★ ★ ★ ★

Follow-up Phase:
Place telephone call to the employer.

1) Introduce yourself
2) Tell purpose of phone call
3) Present 20-second commercial
4) Determine if there is an interest
5) Go to back of contact form and follow appropriate follow-up action.

Messages:
Date/Time: ______________________________
Date/Time: ______________________________
Date/Time: ______________________________

Secretary's name ______________________________

★ ★ ★

FOLLOW-UP ACTION:

❑ **Yes, There Is an Interest:**

Build your marketing plan by gathering as much information as you can about the position. Take notes!

Position/title: ____________________

Position reports to: ____________________

Skills/experience required:

Interview date/time: ____________________

Directions:

★ ★ ★

❑ **No Interest or No Position:**

Ask for a referral!

Name of referred company: ____________________

Name/title of referred employer: ____________________

Address: ____________________

____

____

Telephone Number: ____________________

★ ★ ★

❑ **Has Not Seen Resume:**

Geographically local employer — Suggest that you drop off the resume at a specified date and time. If employer says yes, proceed to ❑ **Yes, There Is an Interest** and build your marketing plan and set up an appointment. If employer responds by saying no interest or nothing open, proceed to ❑ **No Interest or No Position** and ask for a referral.

Geographically distant employer — Establish most expeditious method of sending information to employer with follow-up date and time.

Follow-up date/time: ____________________

If there is no interest or position, ask for a referral.

RMF Employer Contact Form

Contact Dates:
Date mailed: ______________________ Anticipated follow-up date ______________
Actual follow-up date ________________

★ ★ ★ ★ ★

Research Phase:
Organization's Name: ____
Contact Name/Title: ____
Address: ____
____
Telephone Number: ____________________ Fax Number: ____________________
Notes:

Build your cover letter based on the research you have conducted. Place your letter along with your resume in the mail and move to the Mail Phase.

★ ★ ★ ★ ★

Mail Phase:
For geographically local companies, wait 4 to 6 days and then proceed to the Follow-up Phase.
For geographically distant companies wait 5 to 7 days and then proceed to the Follow-up Phase.
Begin doing research on more companies.

★ ★ ★ ★ ★

Follow-up Phase:
Place telephone call to the employer.

1) Introduce yourself
2) Tell purpose of phone call
3) Present 20-second commercial
4) Determine if there is an interest
5) Go to back of contact form and follow appropriate follow-up action.

Messages:
Date/Time: ____
Date/Time: ____
Date/Time: ____

Secretary's name ____

★ ★ ★

FOLLOW-UP ACTION:

❑ **Yes, There Is an Interest:**

Build your marketing plan by gathering as much information as you can about the position. Take notes!

Position/title: ____

Position reports to: ____

Skills/experience required:

Interview date/time: ____

Directions:

★ ★ ★

❑ **No Interest or No Position:**

Ask for a referral!

Name of referred company: ____

Name/title of referred employer: ____

Address: ____

____

____

Telephone Number: ______________________

★ ★ ★

❑ **Has Not Seen Resume:**

Geographically local employer — Suggest that you drop off the resume at a specified date and time. If employer says yes, proceed to ❑ **Yes, There Is an Interest** and build your marketing plan and set up an appointment. If employer responds by saying no interest or nothing open, proceed to ❑ **No Interest or No Position** and ask for a referral.

Geographically distant employer — Establish most expeditious method of sending information to employer with follow-up date and time.

Follow-up date/time: ______________________

If there is no interest or position, ask for a referral.

RMF Employer Contact Form

Contact Dates:
Date mailed: ______________________________ Anticipated follow-up date __________________
Actual follow-up date __________________

★ ★ ★ ★ ★

Research Phase:

Organization's Name: ____
Contact Name/Title: ____
Address: ____

____

Telephone Number: ____________________________ Fax Number: ___________________________

Notes:

Build your cover letter based on the research you have conducted. Place your letter along with your resume in the mail and move to the Mail Phase.

★ ★ ★ ★ ★

Mail Phase:

For geographically local companies, wait 4 to 6 days and then proceed to the Follow-up Phase.
For geographically distant companies wait 5 to 7 days and then proceed to the Follow-up Phase.
Begin doing research on more companies.

★ ★ ★ ★ ★

Follow-up Phase:

Place telephone call to the employer.

1) Introduce yourself
2) Tell purpose of phone call
3) Present 20-second commercial
4) Determine if there is an interest
5) Go to back of contact form and follow appropriate follow-up action.

Messages:
Date/Time: ____
Date/Time: ____
Date/Time: ____

Secretary's name ____

★ ★ ★

FOLLOW-UP ACTION:

❑ **Yes, There Is an Interest:**

Build your marketing plan by gathering as much information as you can about the position. Take notes!

Position/title: ____________________

Position reports to: ____________________

Skills/experience required:

Interview date/time: ____________________

Directions:

★ ★ ★

❑ **No Interest or No Position:**

Ask for a referral!

Name of referred company: ____________________

Name/title of referred employer: ____________________

Address: ____________________

____

____

Telephone Number: ____________________

★ ★ ★

❑ **Has Not Seen Resume:**

Geographically local employer — Suggest that you drop off the resume at a specified date and time. If employer says yes, proceed to ❑ **Yes, There Is an Interest** and build your marketing plan and set up an appointment. If employer responds by saying no interest or nothing open, proceed to ❑ **No Interest or No Position** and ask for a referral.

Geographically distant employer — Establish most expeditious method of sending information to employer with follow-up date and time.

Follow-up date/time: ____________________

If there is no interest or position, ask for a referral.

RMF Employer Contact Form

Contact Dates:

Date mailed: ______________________ Anticipated follow-up date ______________

Actual follow-up date ________________

☆ ☆ ☆ ☆ ☆

Research Phase:

Organization's Name: ____

Contact Name/Title: ____

Address: ____

____

Telephone Number: ____________________ Fax Number: ____________________

Notes:

Build your cover letter based on the research you have conducted. Place your letter along with your resume in the mail and move to the Mail Phase.

☆ ☆ ☆ ☆ ☆

Mail Phase:

For geographically local companies, wait 4 to 6 days and then proceed to the Follow-up Phase.
For geographically distant companies wait 5 to 7 days and then proceed to the Follow-up Phase.
Begin doing research on more companies.

☆ ☆ ☆ ☆ ☆

Follow-up Phase:

Place telephone call to the employer.

1) Introduce yourself
2) Tell purpose of phone call
3) Present 20-second commercial
4) Determine if there is an interest
5) Go to back of contact form and follow appropriate follow-up action.

Messages:

Date/Time: ____

Date/Time: ____

Date/Time: ____

Secretary's name ____

★ ★ ★

Follow-up Action:

❑ **Yes, There Is an Interest:**

Build your marketing plan by gathering as much information as you can about the position. Take notes!

Position/title: ______________________________

Position reports to: ______________________________

Skills/experience required:

Interview date/time: ______________________________

Directions:

★ ★ ★

❑ **No Interest or No Position:**

Ask for a referral!

Name of referred company: ______________________________

Name/title of referred employer: ______________________________

Address: ______________________________

____

____

Telephone Number: ____________________

★ ★ ★

❑ **Has Not Seen Resume:**

Geographically local employer — Suggest that you drop off the resume at a specified date and time. If employer says yes, proceed to ❑ **Yes, There Is an Interest** and build your marketing plan and set up an appointment. If employer responds by saying no interest or nothing open, proceed to ❑ **No Interest or No Position** and ask for a referral.

Geographically distant employer — Establish most expeditious method of sending information to employer with follow-up date and time.

Follow-up date/time: ____________________

If there is no interest or position, ask for a referral.

RMF Employer Contact Form

Contact Dates:

Date mailed: ______________________ Anticipated follow-up date ______________

Actual follow-up date ______________

★ ★ ★ ★ ★

Research Phase:

Organization's Name: ____

Contact Name/Title: ____

Address: ____

____

Telephone Number: ______________________ Fax Number: ______________________

Notes:

Build your cover letter based on the research you have conducted. Place your letter along with your resume in the mail and move to the Mail Phase.

★ ★ ★ ★ ★

Mail Phase:

For geographically local companies, wait 4 to 6 days and then proceed to the Follow-up Phase.
For geographically distant companies wait 5 to 7 days and then proceed to the Follow-up Phase.
Begin doing research on more companies.

★ ★ ★ ★ ★

Follow-up Phase:

Place telephone call to the employer.

1) Introduce yourself
2) Tell purpose of phone call
3) Present 20-second commercial
4) Determine if there is an interest
5) Go to back of contact form and follow appropriate follow-up action.

Messages:

Date/Time: ____

Date/Time: ____

Date/Time: ____

Secretary's name ____

★ ★ ★

Follow-up Action:

❑ **Yes, There Is an Interest:**

Build your marketing plan by gathering as much information as you can about the position. Take notes!

Position/title: ____________________

Position reports to: ____________________

Skills/experience required:

Interview date/time: ____________________

Directions:

★ ★ ★

❑ **No Interest or No Position:**

Ask for a referral!

Name of referred company: ____________________

Name/title of referred employer: ____________________

Address: ____________________

____

____

Telephone Number: ____________________

★ ★ ★

❑ **Has Not Seen Resume:**

Geographically local employer — Suggest that you drop off the resume at a specified date and time. If employer says yes, proceed to ❑ **Yes, There Is an Interest** and build your marketing plan and set up an appointment. If employer responds by saying no interest or nothing open, proceed to ❑ **No Interest or No Position** and ask for a referral.

Geographically distant employer — Establish most expeditious method of sending information to employer with follow-up date and time.

Follow-up date/time: ____________________

If there is no interest or position, ask for a referral.

RMF Employer Contact Form

Contact Dates:

Date mailed: ______________________ Anticipated follow-up date ______________

Actual follow-up date ________________

★ ★ ★ ★ ★

Research Phase:

Organization's Name: ____

Contact Name/Title: ____

Address: ____

____

Telephone Number: ____________________ Fax Number: ____________________

Notes:

Build your cover letter based on the research you have conducted. Place your letter along with your resume in the mail and move to the Mail Phase.

★ ★ ★ ★ ★

Mail Phase:

For geographically local companies, wait 4 to 6 days and then proceed to the Follow-up Phase. For geographically distant companies wait 5 to 7 days and then proceed to the Follow-up Phase. Begin doing research on more companies.

★ ★ ★ ★ ★

Follow-up Phase:

Place telephone call to the employer.

1) Introduce yourself
2) Tell purpose of phone call
3) Present 20-second commercial
4) Determine if there is an interest
5) Go to back of contact form and follow appropriate follow-up action.

Messages:

Date/Time: ____

Date/Time: ____

Date/Time: ____

Secretary's name ____

★ ★ ★

Follow-up Action:

❑ **Yes, There Is an Interest:**

Build your marketing plan by gathering as much information as you can about the position. Take notes!

Position/title: ______________________________

Position reports to: ______________________________

Skills/experience required:

Interview date/time: ______________________________

Directions:

★ ★ ★

❑ **No Interest or No Position:**

Ask for a referral!

Name of referred company: ______________________________

Name/title of referred employer: ______________________________

Address: ______________________________

____

____

Telephone Number: ____________________

★ ★ ★

❑ **Has Not Seen Resume:**

Geographically local employer — Suggest that you drop off the resume at a specified date and time. If employer says yes, proceed to ❑ **Yes, There Is an Interest** and build your marketing plan and set up an appointment. If employer responds by saying no interest or nothing open, proceed to ❑ **No Interest or No Position** and ask for a referral.

Geographically distant employer — Establish most expeditious method of sending information to employer with follow-up date and time.

Follow-up date/time: ____________________

If there is no interest or position, ask for a referral.

RMF Employer Contact Form

Contact Dates:
Date mailed: ____________________ Anticipated follow-up date ____________
Actual follow-up date ____________

☆ ☆ ☆ ☆ ☆

Research Phase:
Organization's Name: ______________________________
Contact Name/Title: ______________________________
Address: ______________________________
____
Telephone Number: ____________________ Fax Number: ____________________
Notes:

Build your cover letter based on the research you have conducted. Place your letter along with your resume in the mail and move to the Mail Phase.

☆ ☆ ☆ ☆ ☆

Mail Phase:
For geographically local companies, wait 4 to 6 days and then proceed to the Follow-up Phase.
For geographically distant companies wait 5 to 7 days and then proceed to the Follow-up Phase.
Begin doing research on more companies.

☆ ☆ ☆ ☆ ☆

Follow-up Phase:
Place telephone call to the employer.

1) Introduce yourself
2) Tell purpose of phone call
3) Present 20-second commercial
4) Determine if there is an interest
5) Go to back of contact form and follow appropriate follow-up action.

Messages:
Date/Time: ______________________________
Date/Time: ______________________________
Date/Time: ______________________________

Secretary's name ______________________________

★ ★ ★

Follow-up Action:

❑ **Yes, There Is an Interest:**

Build your marketing plan by gathering as much information as you can about the position. Take notes!

Position/title: ____________________

Position reports to: ____________________

Skills/experience required:

Interview date/time: ____________________

Directions:

★ ★ ★

❑ **No Interest or No Position:**

Ask for a referral!

Name of referred company: ____________________

Name/title of referred employer: ____________________

Address: ____________________

____

____

Telephone Number: ____________________

★ ★ ★

❑ **Has Not Seen Resume:**

Geographically local employer — Suggest that you drop off the resume at a specified date and time. If employer says yes, proceed to ❑ **Yes, There Is an Interest** and build your marketing plan and set up an appointment. If employer responds by saying no interest or nothing open, proceed to ❑ **No Interest or No Position** and ask for a referral.

Geographically distant employer — Establish most expeditious method of sending information to employer with follow-up date and time.

Follow-up date/time: ____________________

If there is no interest or position, ask for a referral.

RMF Employer Contact Form

Contact Dates:

Date mailed: ______________________ Anticipated follow-up date ______________

Actual follow-up date ______________

★ ★ ★ ★ ★

Research Phase:

Organization's Name: ____

Contact Name/Title: ____

Address: ____

____

Telephone Number: ____________________ Fax Number: ____________________

Notes:

Build your cover letter based on the research you have conducted. Place your letter along with your resume in the mail and move to the Mail Phase.

★ ★ ★ ★ ★

Mail Phase:

For geographically local companies, wait 4 to 6 days and then proceed to the Follow-up Phase.
For geographically distant companies wait 5 to 7 days and then proceed to the Follow-up Phase.
Begin doing research on more companies.

★ ★ ★ ★ ★

Follow-up Phase:

Place telephone call to the employer.

1) Introduce yourself
2) Tell purpose of phone call
3) Present 20-second commercial
4) Determine if there is an interest
5) Go to back of contact form and follow appropriate follow-up action.

Messages:

Date/Time: ____

Date/Time: ____

Date/Time: ____

Secretary's name ____

★ ★ ★

Follow-up Action:

❑ **Yes, There Is an Interest:**

Build your marketing plan by gathering as much information as you can about the position. Take notes!

Position/title: ______________________________

Position reports to: ______________________________

Skills/experience required:

Interview date/time: ______________________________

Directions:

★ ★ ★

❑ **No Interest or No Position:**

Ask for a referral!

Name of referred company: ______________________________

Name/title of referred employer: ______________________________

Address: ______________________________

____

____

Telephone Number: ____________________

★ ★ ★

❑ **Has Not Seen Resume:**

Geographically local employer — Suggest that you drop off the resume at a specified date and time. If employer says yes, proceed to ❑ **Yes, There Is an Interest** and build your marketing plan and set up an appointment. If employer responds by saying no interest or nothing open, proceed to ❑ **No Interest or No Position** and ask for a referral.

Geographically distant employer — Establish most expeditious method of sending information to employer with follow-up date and time.

Follow-up date/time: ____________________

If there is no interest or position, ask for a referral.

RMF Employer Contact Form

Contact Dates:

Date mailed: ______________________ Anticipated follow-up date ______________

Actual follow-up date __________________

☆ ☆ ☆ ☆ ☆

RESEARCH PHASE:

Organization's Name: ______________________________________

Contact Name/Title: ______________________________________

Address: ______________________________________

____

Telephone Number: ______________________ Fax Number: ______________________

Notes:

Build your cover letter based on the research you have conducted. Place your letter along with your resume in the mail and move to the Mail Phase.

☆ ☆ ☆ ☆ ☆

MAIL PHASE:

For geographically local companies, wait 4 to 6 days and then proceed to the Follow-up Phase.
For geographically distant companies wait 5 to 7 days and then proceed to the Follow-up Phase.
Begin doing research on more companies.

☆ ☆ ☆ ☆ ☆

FOLLOW-UP PHASE:

Place telephone call to the employer.

1) Introduce yourself
2) Tell purpose of phone call
3) Present 20-second commercial
4) Determine if there is an interest
5) Go to back of contact form and follow appropriate follow-up action.

Messages:

Date/Time: ______________________________________

Date/Time: ______________________________________

Date/Time: ______________________________________

Secretary's name ______________________________________

★ ★ ★

FOLLOW-UP ACTION:

❑ **Yes, There Is an Interest:**

Build your marketing plan by gathering as much information as you can about the position. Take notes!

Position/title: ______________________________

Position reports to: ______________________________

Skills/experience required:

Interview date/time: ______________________________

Directions:

★ ★ ★

❑ **No Interest or No Position:**

Ask for a referral!

Name of referred company: ______________________________

Name/title of referred employer: ______________________________

Address: ______________________________

____

____

Telephone Number: ____________________

★ ★ ★

❑ **Has Not Seen Resume:**

Geographically local employer — Suggest that you drop off the resume at a specified date and time. If employer says yes, proceed to ❑ **Yes, There Is an Interest** and build your marketing plan and set up an appointment. If employer responds by saying no interest or nothing open, proceed to ❑ **No Interest or No Position** and ask for a referral.

Geographically distant employer — Establish most expeditious method of sending information to employer with follow-up date and time.

Follow-up date/time: ____________________

If there is no interest or position, ask for a referral.

RMF Employer Contact Form

Contact Dates:

Date mailed: ______________________________ Anticipated follow-up date ______________

Actual follow-up date ______________

★ ★ ★ ★ ★

Research Phase:

Organization's Name: ____

Contact Name/Title: ____

Address: ____

____

Telephone Number: ______________________ Fax Number: ______________________

Notes:

Build your cover letter based on the research you have conducted. Place your letter along with your resume in the mail and move to the Mail Phase.

★ ★ ★ ★ ★

Mail Phase:

For geographically local companies, wait 4 to 6 days and then proceed to the Follow-up Phase. For geographically distant companies wait 5 to 7 days and then proceed to the Follow-up Phase. Begin doing research on more companies.

★ ★ ★ ★ ★

Follow-up Phase:

Place telephone call to the employer.

1) Introduce yourself
2) Tell purpose of phone call
3) Present 20-second commercial
4) Determine if there is an interest
5) Go to back of contact form and follow appropriate follow-up action.

Messages:

Date/Time: ____

Date/Time: ____

Date/Time: ____

Secretary's name ____

★ ★ ★

FOLLOW-UP ACTION:

❑ **Yes, There Is an Interest:**

Build your marketing plan by gathering as much information as you can about the position. Take notes!

Position/title: ____________________

Position reports to: ____________________

Skills/experience required:

Interview date/time: ____________________

Directions:

★ ★ ★

❑ **No Interest or No Position:**

Ask for a referral!

Name of referred company: ____________________

Name/title of referred employer: ____________________

Address: ____________________

____

____

Telephone Number: ____________________

★ ★ ★

❑ **Has Not Seen Resume:**

Geographically local employer — Suggest that you drop off the resume at a specified date and time. If employer says yes, proceed to ❑ **Yes, There Is an Interest** and build your marketing plan and set up an appointment. If employer responds by saying no interest or nothing open, proceed to ❑ **No Interest or No Position** and ask for a referral.

Geographically distant employer — Establish most expeditious method of sending information to employer with follow-up date and time.

Follow-up date/time: ____________________

If there is no interest or position, ask for a referral.

RMF Employer Contact Form

Contact Dates:
Date mailed: ______________________ Anticipated follow-up date ______________
Actual follow-up date ______________

☆ ☆ ☆ ☆ ☆

Research Phase:
Organization's Name: ______________________________
Contact Name/Title: ______________________________
Address: ______________________________
____
Telephone Number: ______________________ Fax Number: ______________________
Notes:

Build your cover letter based on the research you have conducted. Place your letter along with your resume in the mail and move to the Mail Phase.

☆ ☆ ☆ ☆ ☆

Mail Phase:
For geographically local companies, wait 4 to 6 days and then proceed to the Follow-up Phase.
For geographically distant companies wait 5 to 7 days and then proceed to the Follow-up Phase.
Begin doing research on more companies.

☆ ☆ ☆ ☆ ☆

Follow-up Phase:
Place telephone call to the employer.

1) Introduce yourself
2) Tell purpose of phone call
3) Present 20-second commercial
4) Determine if there is an interest
5) Go to back of contact form and follow appropriate follow-up action.

Messages:
Date/Time: ______________________________
Date/Time: ______________________________
Date/Time: ______________________________

Secretary's name ______________________________

★ ★ ★

FOLLOW-UP ACTION:

❑ **Yes, There Is an Interest:**

Build your marketing plan by gathering as much information as you can about the position. Take notes!

Position/title: ______________________________

Position reports to: ______________________________

Skills/experience required:

Interview date/time: ______________________________

Directions:

★ ★ ★

❑ **No Interest or No Position:**

Ask for a referral!

Name of referred company: ______________________________

Name/title of referred employer: ______________________________

Address: ______________________________

____

____

Telephone Number: ____________________

★ ★ ★

❑ **Has Not Seen Resume:**

Geographically local employer — Suggest that you drop off the resume at a specified date and time. If employer says yes, proceed to ❑ **Yes, There Is an Interest** and build your marketing plan and set up an appointment. If employer responds by saying no interest or nothing open, proceed to ❑ **No Interest or No Position** and ask for a referral.

Geographically distant employer — Establish most expeditious method of sending information to employer with follow-up date and time.

Follow-up date/time: ____________________

If there is no interest or position, ask for a referral.

RMF Employer Contact Form

Contact Dates:

Date mailed: ____________ Anticipated follow-up date ____________

Actual follow-up date ____________

★ ★ ★ ★ ★

Research Phase:

Organization's Name: ____________

Contact Name/Title: ____________

Address: ____________

____

Telephone Number: ____________ Fax Number: ____________

Notes:

Build your cover letter based on the research you have conducted. Place your letter along with your resume in the mail and move to the Mail Phase.

★ ★ ★ ★ ★

Mail Phase:

For geographically local companies, wait 4 to 6 days and then proceed to the Follow-up Phase. For geographically distant companies wait 5 to 7 days and then proceed to the Follow-up Phase. Begin doing research on more companies.

★ ★ ★ ★ ★

Follow-up Phase:

Place telephone call to the employer.

1) Introduce yourself
2) Tell purpose of phone call
3) Present 20-second commercial
4) Determine if there is an interest
5) Go to back of contact form and follow appropriate follow-up action.

Messages:

Date/Time: ____________

Date/Time: ____________

Date/Time: ____________

Secretary's name ____________

★ ★ ★

FOLLOW-UP ACTION:

❑ **Yes, There Is an Interest:**

Build your marketing plan by gathering as much information as you can about the position. Take notes!

Position/title: ____________________

Position reports to: ____________________

Skills/experience required:

Interview date/time: ____________________

Directions:

★ ★ ★

❑ **No Interest or No Position:**

Ask for a referral!

Name of referred company: ____________________

Name/title of referred employer: ____________________

Address: ____________________

____

____

Telephone Number: ____________________

★ ★ ★

❑ **Has Not Seen Resume:**

Geographically local employer — Suggest that you drop off the resume at a specified date and time. If employer says yes, proceed to ❑ **Yes, There Is an Interest** and build your marketing plan and set up an appointment. If employer responds by saying no interest or nothing open, proceed to ❑ **No Interest or No Position** and ask for a referral.

Geographically distant employer — Establish most expeditious method of sending information to employer with follow-up date and time.

Follow-up date/time: ____________________

If there is no interest or position, ask for a referral.

RMF EMPLOYER CONTACT FORM

Contact Dates:
Date mailed: ______________________________ Anticipated follow-up date __________________
Actual follow-up date _______________________

★ ★ ★ ★ ★

RESEARCH PHASE:
Organization's Name: ____
Contact Name/Title: ____
Address: ____
____
Telephone Number: ____________________________ Fax Number: ___________________________
Notes:

Build your cover letter based on the research you have conducted. Place your letter along with your resume in the mail and move to the Mail Phase.

★ ★ ★ ★ ★

MAIL PHASE:
For geographically local companies, wait 4 to 6 days and then proceed to the Follow-up Phase.
For geographically distant companies wait 5 to 7 days and then proceed to the Follow-up Phase.
Begin doing research on more companies.

★ ★ ★ ★ ★

FOLLOW-UP PHASE:
Place telephone call to the employer.

1) Introduce yourself
2) Tell purpose of phone call
3) Present 20-second commercial
4) Determine if there is an interest
5) Go to back of contact form and follow appropriate follow-up action.

Messages:
Date/Time: ____
Date/Time: ____
Date/Time: ____

Secretary's name ____

★ ★ ★

Follow-up Action:

❑ **Yes, There Is an Interest:**

Build your marketing plan by gathering as much information as you can about the position. Take notes!

Position/title: ____________________

Position reports to: ____________________

Skills/experience required:

Interview date/time: ____________________

Directions:

★ ★ ★

❑ **No Interest or No Position:**

Ask for a referral!

Name of referred company: ____________________

Name/title of referred employer: ____________________

Address: ____________________

____

____

Telephone Number: ____________________

★ ★ ★

❑ **Has Not Seen Resume:**

Geographically local employer — Suggest that you drop off the resume at a specified date and time. If employer says yes, proceed to ❑ **Yes, There Is an Interest** and build your marketing plan and set up an appointment. If employer responds by saying no interest or nothing open, proceed to ❑ **No Interest or No Position** and ask for a referral.

Geographically distant employer — Establish most expeditious method of sending information to employer with follow-up date and time.

Follow-up date/time: ____________________

If there is no interest or position, ask for a referral.

RMF EMPLOYER CONTACT FORM

Contact Dates:
Date mailed: ____________________ Anticipated follow-up date ____________
Actual follow-up date ____________

★ ★ ★ ★ ★

RESEARCH PHASE:
Organization's Name: ____________________
Contact Name/Title: ____________________
Address: ____________________
____
Telephone Number: ____________________ Fax Number: ____________________
Notes:

Build your cover letter based on the research you have conducted. Place your letter along with your resume in the mail and move to the Mail Phase.

★ ★ ★ ★ ★

MAIL PHASE:
For geographically local companies, wait 4 to 6 days and then proceed to the Follow-up Phase.
For geographically distant companies wait 5 to 7 days and then proceed to the Follow-up Phase.
Begin doing research on more companies.

★ ★ ★ ★ ★

FOLLOW-UP PHASE:
Place telephone call to the employer.

1) Introduce yourself
2) Tell purpose of phone call
3) Present 20-second commercial
4) Determine if there is an interest
5) Go to back of contact form and follow appropriate follow-up action.

Messages:
Date/Time: ____________________
Date/Time: ____________________
Date/Time: ____________________

Secretary's name ____________________

★ ★ ★

FOLLOW-UP ACTION:

❑ **Yes, There Is an Interest:**

Build your marketing plan by gathering as much information as you can about the position. Take notes!

Position/title: ____________________

Position reports to: ____________________

Skills/experience required:

Interview date/time: ____________________

Directions:

★ ★ ★

❑ **No Interest or No Position:**

Ask for a referral!

Name of referred company: ____________________

Name/title of referred employer: ____________________

Address: ____________________

____

____

Telephone Number: ____________________

★ ★ ★

❑ **Has Not Seen Resume:**

Geographically local employer — Suggest that you drop off the resume at a specified date and time. If employer says yes, proceed to ❑ **Yes, There Is an Interest** and build your marketing plan and set up an appointment. If employer responds by saying no interest or nothing open, proceed to ❑ **No Interest or No Position** and ask for a referral.

Geographically distant employer — Establish most expeditious method of sending information to employer with follow-up date and time.

Follow-up date/time: ____________________

If there is no interest or position, ask for a referral.

RMF Employer Contact Form

Contact Dates:
Date mailed: ______________________ Anticipated follow-up date ______________
Actual follow-up date ______________

☆ ☆ ☆ ☆ ☆

Research Phase:
Organization's Name: ______________________
Contact Name/Title: ______________________
Address: ______________________
____
Telephone Number: ______________________ Fax Number: ______________________
Notes:

Build your cover letter based on the research you have conducted. Place your letter along with your resume in the mail and move to the Mail Phase.

☆ ☆ ☆ ☆ ☆

Mail Phase:
For geographically local companies, wait 4 to 6 days and then proceed to the Follow-up Phase.
For geographically distant companies wait 5 to 7 days and then proceed to the Follow-up Phase.
Begin doing research on more companies.

☆ ☆ ☆ ☆ ☆

Follow-up Phase:
Place telephone call to the employer.

1) Introduce yourself
2) Tell purpose of phone call
3) Present 20-second commercial
4) Determine if there is an interest
5) Go to back of contact form and follow appropriate follow-up action.

Messages:
Date/Time: ______________________
Date/Time: ______________________
Date/Time: ______________________

Secretary's name ______________________

★ ★ ★

FOLLOW-UP ACTION:

❑ **Yes, There Is an Interest:**

Build your marketing plan by gathering as much information as you can about the position. Take notes!

Position/title: ______________________________

Position reports to: ______________________________

Skills/experience required:

Interview date/time: ______________________________

Directions:

★ ★ ★

❑ **No Interest or No Position:**

Ask for a referral!

Name of referred company: ______________________________

Name/title of referred employer: ______________________________

Address: ______________________________

____

____

Telephone Number: ____________________

★ ★ ★

❑ **Has Not Seen Resume:**

Geographically local employer — Suggest that you drop off the resume at a specified date and time. If employer says yes, proceed to ❑ **Yes, There Is an Interest** and build your marketing plan and set up an appointment. If employer responds by saying no interest or nothing open, proceed to ❑ **No Interest or No Position** and ask for a referral.

Geographically distant employer — Establish most expeditious method of sending information to employer with follow-up date and time.

Follow-up date/time: ____________________

If there is no interest or position, ask for a referral.

RMF Employer Contact Form

Contact Dates:

Date mailed: ______________________ Anticipated follow-up date ______________

Actual follow-up date ______________

★ ★ ★ ★ ★

Research Phase:

Organization's Name: ______________________________________

Contact Name/Title: ______________________________________

Address: ______________________________________

____

Telephone Number: ____________________ Fax Number: ____________________

Notes:

Build your cover letter based on the research you have conducted. Place your letter along with your resume in the mail and move to the Mail Phase.

★ ★ ★ ★ ★

Mail Phase:

For geographically local companies, wait 4 to 6 days and then proceed to the Follow-up Phase. For geographically distant companies wait 5 to 7 days and then proceed to the Follow-up Phase. Begin doing research on more companies.

★ ★ ★ ★ ★

Follow-up Phase:

Place telephone call to the employer.

1) Introduce yourself
2) Tell purpose of phone call
3) Present 20-second commercial
4) Determine if there is an interest
5) Go to back of contact form and follow appropriate follow-up action.

Messages:

Date/Time: ______________________________________

Date/Time: ______________________________________

Date/Time: ______________________________________

Secretary's name ______________________________________

★ ★ ★

FOLLOW-UP ACTION:

❑ **Yes, There Is an Interest:**

Build your marketing plan by gathering as much information as you can about the position. Take notes!

Position/title: ______________________________

Position reports to: ______________________________

Skills/experience required:

Interview date/time: ______________________________

Directions:

★ ★ ★

❑ **No Interest or No Position:**

Ask for a referral!

Name of referred company: ______________________________

Name/title of referred employer: ______________________________

Address: ______________________________

____

____

Telephone Number: ____________________

★ ★ ★

❑ **Has Not Seen Resume:**

Geographically local employer — Suggest that you drop off the resume at a specified date and time. If employer says yes, proceed to ❑ **Yes, There Is an Interest** and build your marketing plan and set up an appointment. If employer responds by saying no interest or nothing open, proceed to ❑ **No Interest or No Position** and ask for a referral.

Geographically distant employer — Establish most expeditious method of sending information to employer with follow-up date and time.

Follow-up date/time: ____________________

If there is no interest or position, ask for a referral.

RMF Employer Contact Form

Contact Dates:
Date mailed: ______________________ Anticipated follow-up date ______________
Actual follow-up date ______________

★ ★ ★ ★ ★

Research Phase:
Organization's Name: ______________________________________
Contact Name/Title: ______________________________________
Address: ______________________________________
____
Telephone Number: ____________________ Fax Number: ____________________
Notes:

Build your cover letter based on the research you have conducted. Place your letter along with your resume in the mail and move to the Mail Phase.

★ ★ ★ ★ ★

Mail Phase:
For geographically local companies, wait 4 to 6 days and then proceed to the Follow-up Phase.
For geographically distant companies wait 5 to 7 days and then proceed to the Follow-up Phase.
Begin doing research on more companies.

★ ★ ★ ★ ★

Follow-up Phase:
Place telephone call to the employer.

1) Introduce yourself
2) Tell purpose of phone call
3) Present 20-second commercial
4) Determine if there is an interest
5) Go to back of contact form and follow appropriate follow-up action.

Messages:
Date/Time: ______________________________________
Date/Time: ______________________________________
Date/Time: ______________________________________

Secretary's name ______________________________________

★ ★ ★

FOLLOW-UP ACTION:

❑ **Yes, There Is an Interest:**

Build your marketing plan by gathering as much information as you can about the position. Take notes!

Position/title: ______________________________

Position reports to: ______________________________

Skills/experience required:

Interview date/time: ______________________________

Directions:

★ ★ ★

❑ **No Interest or No Position:**

Ask for a referral!

Name of referred company: ______________________________

Name/title of referred employer: ______________________________

Address: ______________________________

____

____

Telephone Number: ____________________

★ ★ ★

❑ **Has Not Seen Resume:**

Geographically local employer — Suggest that you drop off the resume at a specified date and time. If employer says yes, proceed to ❑ **Yes, There Is an Interest** and build your marketing plan and set up an appointment. If employer responds by saying no interest or nothing open, proceed to ❑ **No Interest or No Position** and ask for a referral.

Geographically distant employer — Establish most expeditious method of sending information to employer with follow-up date and time.

Follow-up date/time: ____________________

If there is no interest or position, ask for a referral.

RMF Employer Contact Form

Contact Dates:
Date mailed: ______________________________ Anticipated follow-up date ________________
Actual follow-up date ________________

★ ★ ★ ★ ★

Research Phase:

Organization's Name: ____
Contact Name/Title: ____
Address: ____
____
Telephone Number: ________________________ Fax Number: ________________________
Notes:

Build your cover letter based on the research you have conducted. Place your letter along with your resume in the mail and move to the Mail Phase.

★ ★ ★ ★ ★

Mail Phase:

For geographically local companies, wait 4 to 6 days and then proceed to the Follow-up Phase.
For geographically distant companies wait 5 to 7 days and then proceed to the Follow-up Phase.
Begin doing research on more companies.

★ ★ ★ ★ ★

Follow-up Phase:

Place telephone call to the employer.

1) Introduce yourself
2) Tell purpose of phone call
3) Present 20-second commercial
4) Determine if there is an interest
5) Go to back of contact form and follow appropriate follow-up action.

Messages:
Date/Time: ____
Date/Time: ____
Date/Time: ____

Secretary's name ____

★ ★ ★

Follow-up Action:

❑ **Yes, There Is an Interest:**

Build your marketing plan by gathering as much information as you can about the position. Take notes!

Position/title: ______________________________

Position reports to: ______________________________

Skills/experience required:

Interview date/time: ______________________________

Directions:

★ ★ ★

❑ **No Interest or No Position:**

Ask for a referral!

Name of referred company: ______________________________

Name/title of referred employer: ______________________________

Address: ______________________________

____

____

Telephone Number: ____________________

★ ★ ★

❑ **Has Not Seen Resume:**

Geographically local employer — Suggest that you drop off the resume at a specified date and time. If employer says yes, proceed to ❑ **Yes, There Is an Interest** and build your marketing plan and set up an appointment. If employer responds by saying no interest or nothing open, proceed to ❑ **No Interest or No Position** and ask for a referral.

Geographically distant employer — Establish most expeditious method of sending information to employer with follow-up date and time.

Follow-up date/time: ____________________

If there is no interest or position, ask for a referral.

RMF Employer Contact Form

Contact Dates:
Date mailed: ______________________ Anticipated follow-up date ______________
Actual follow-up date ________________

★ ★ ★ ★ ★

Research Phase:
Organization's Name: ____
Contact Name/Title: ____
Address: ____
____
Telephone Number: ____________________ Fax Number: ____________________
Notes:

Build your cover letter based on the research you have conducted. Place your letter along with your resume in the mail and move to the Mail Phase.

★ ★ ★ ★ ★

Mail Phase:
For geographically local companies, wait 4 to 6 days and then proceed to the Follow-up Phase.
For geographically distant companies wait 5 to 7 days and then proceed to the Follow-up Phase.
Begin doing research on more companies.

★ ★ ★ ★ ★

Follow-up Phase:
Place telephone call to the employer.

1) Introduce yourself
2) Tell purpose of phone call
3) Present 20-second commercial
4) Determine if there is an interest
5) Go to back of contact form and follow appropriate follow-up action.

Messages:
Date/Time: ____
Date/Time: ____
Date/Time: ____

Secretary's name ____

★ ★ ★

Follow-up Action:

❑ **Yes, There Is an Interest:**

Build your marketing plan by gathering as much information as you can about the position. Take notes!

Position/title: ____________________

Position reports to: ____________________

Skills/experience required:

Interview date/time: ____________________

Directions:

★ ★ ★

❑ **No Interest or No Position:**

Ask for a referral!

Name of referred company: ____________________

Name/title of referred employer: ____________________

Address: ____________________

____

____

Telephone Number: ____________________

★ ★ ★

❑ **Has Not Seen Resume:**

Geographically local employer — Suggest that you drop off the resume at a specified date and time. If employer says yes, proceed to ❑ **Yes, There Is an Interest** and build your marketing plan and set up an appointment. If employer responds by saying no interest or nothing open, proceed to ❑ **No Interest or No Position** and ask for a referral.

Geographically distant employer — Establish most expeditious method of sending information to employer with follow-up date and time.

Follow-up date/time: ____________________

If there is no interest or position, ask for a referral.

RMF Employer Contact Form

Contact Dates:
Date mailed: ______________________ Anticipated follow-up date ______________
Actual follow-up date ______________

☆ ☆ ☆ ☆ ☆

Research Phase:
Organization's Name: ______________________________
Contact Name/Title: ______________________________
Address: ______________________________
____
Telephone Number: ______________________ Fax Number: ______________
Notes:

Build your cover letter based on the research you have conducted. Place your letter along with your resume in the mail and move to the Mail Phase.

☆ ☆ ☆ ☆ ☆

Mail Phase:
For geographically local companies, wait 4 to 6 days and then proceed to the Follow-up Phase.
For geographically distant companies wait 5 to 7 days and then proceed to the Follow-up Phase.
Begin doing research on more companies.

☆ ☆ ☆ ☆ ☆

Follow-up Phase:
Place telephone call to the employer.

1) Introduce yourself
2) Tell purpose of phone call
3) Present 20-second commercial
4) Determine if there is an interest
5) Go to back of contact form and follow appropriate follow-up action.

Messages:
Date/Time: ______________________________
Date/Time: ______________________________
Date/Time: ______________________________

Secretary's name ______________________________

★ ★ ★

FOLLOW-UP ACTION:

❑ **Yes, There Is an Interest:**

Build your marketing plan by gathering as much information as you can about the position. Take notes!

Position/title: ____________________

Position reports to: ____________________

Skills/experience required:

Interview date/time: ____________________

Directions:

★ ★ ★

❑ **No Interest or No Position:**

Ask for a referral!

Name of referred company: ____________________

Name/title of referred employer: ____________________

Address: ____________________

____

____

Telephone Number: ____________________

★ ★ ★

❑ **Has Not Seen Resume:**

Geographically local employer — Suggest that you drop off the resume at a specified date and time. If employer says yes, proceed to ❑ **Yes, There Is an Interest** and build your marketing plan and set up an appointment. If employer responds by saying no interest or nothing open, proceed to ❑ **No Interest or No Position** and ask for a referral.

Geographically distant employer — Establish most expeditious method of sending information to employer with follow-up date and time.

Follow-up date/time: ____________________

If there is no interest or position, ask for a referral.

RMF Employer Contact Form

Contact Dates:
Date mailed: ______________________ Anticipated follow-up date ______________
Actual follow-up date ________________

★ ★ ★ ★ ★

Research Phase:
Organization's Name: ____
Contact Name/Title: ____
Address: ____
____
Telephone Number: ____________________ Fax Number: ____________________
Notes:

Build your cover letter based on the research you have conducted. Place your letter along with your resume in the mail and move to the Mail Phase.

★ ★ ★ ★ ★

Mail Phase:
For geographically local companies, wait 4 to 6 days and then proceed to the Follow-up Phase.
For geographically distant companies wait 5 to 7 days and then proceed to the Follow-up Phase.
Begin doing research on more companies.

★ ★ ★ ★ ★

Follow-up Phase:
Place telephone call to the employer.

1) Introduce yourself
2) Tell purpose of phone call
3) Present 20-second commercial
4) Determine if there is an interest
5) Go to back of contact form and follow appropriate follow-up action.

Messages:
Date/Time: ____
Date/Time: ____
Date/Time: ____

Secretary's name ____

★ ★ ★

FOLLOW-UP ACTION:

❑ **Yes, There Is an Interest:**

Build your marketing plan by gathering as much information as you can about the position. Take notes!

Position/title: ____________________

Position reports to: ____________________

Skills/experience required:

Interview date/time: ____________________

Directions:

★ ★ ★

❑ **No Interest or No Position:**

Ask for a referral!

Name of referred company: ____________________

Name/title of referred employer: ____________________

Address: ____________________

____

____

Telephone Number: ____________________

★ ★ ★

❑ **Has Not Seen Resume:**

Geographically local employer — Suggest that you drop off the resume at a specified date and time. If employer says yes, proceed to ❑ **Yes, There Is an Interest** and build your marketing plan and set up an appointment. If employer responds by saying no interest or nothing open, proceed to ❑ **No Interest or No Position** and ask for a referral.

Geographically distant employer — Establish most expeditious method of sending information to employer with follow-up date and time.

Follow-up date/time: ____________________

If there is no interest or position, ask for a referral.

RMF Employer Contact Form

Contact Dates:

Date mailed: ______________________ Anticipated follow-up date ______________

Actual follow-up date ______________

☆ ☆ ☆ ☆ ☆

Research Phase:

Organization's Name: ______________________________

Contact Name/Title: ______________________________

Address: ______________________________

____

Telephone Number: ______________________ Fax Number: ______________________

Notes:

Build your cover letter based on the research you have conducted. Place your letter along with your resume in the mail and move to the Mail Phase.

☆ ☆ ☆ ☆ ☆

Mail Phase:

For geographically local companies, wait 4 to 6 days and then proceed to the Follow-up Phase. For geographically distant companies wait 5 to 7 days and then proceed to the Follow-up Phase. Begin doing research on more companies.

☆ ☆ ☆ ☆ ☆

Follow-up Phase:

Place telephone call to the employer.

1) Introduce yourself
2) Tell purpose of phone call
3) Present 20-second commercial
4) Determine if there is an interest
5) Go to back of contact form and follow appropriate follow-up action.

Messages:

Date/Time: ______________________________

Date/Time: ______________________________

Date/Time: ______________________________

Secretary's name ______________________________

★ ★ ★

FOLLOW-UP ACTION:

❑ **Yes, There Is an Interest:**

Build your marketing plan by gathering as much information as you can about the position. Take notes!

Position/title: ____________________

Position reports to: ____________________

Skills/experience required:

Interview date/time: ____________________

Directions:

★ ★ ★

❑ **No Interest or No Position:**

Ask for a referral!

Name of referred company: ____________________

Name/title of referred employer: ____________________

Address: ____________________

____

____

Telephone Number: ____________________

★ ★ ★

❑ **Has Not Seen Resume:**

Geographically local employer — Suggest that you drop off the resume at a specified date and time. If employer says yes, proceed to ❑ **Yes, There Is an Interest** and build your marketing plan and set up an appointment. If employer responds by saying no interest or nothing open, proceed to ❑ **No Interest or No Position** and ask for a referral.

Geographically distant employer — Establish most expeditious method of sending information to employer with follow-up date and time.

Follow-up date/time: ____________________

If there is no interest or position, ask for a referral.

RMF Employer Contact Form

Contact Dates:

Date mailed: ______________________ Anticipated follow-up date ______________

Actual follow-up date ________________

★ ★ ★ ★ ★

Research Phase:

Organization's Name: ____

Contact Name/Title: ____

Address: ____

____

Telephone Number: ______________________ Fax Number: ____________________

Notes:

Build your cover letter based on the research you have conducted. Place your letter along with your resume in the mail and move to the Mail Phase.

★ ★ ★ ★ ★

Mail Phase:

For geographically local companies, wait 4 to 6 days and then proceed to the Follow-up Phase. For geographically distant companies wait 5 to 7 days and then proceed to the Follow-up Phase. Begin doing research on more companies.

★ ★ ★ ★ ★

Follow-up Phase:

Place telephone call to the employer.

1) Introduce yourself
2) Tell purpose of phone call
3) Present 20-second commercial
4) Determine if there is an interest
5) Go to back of contact form and follow appropriate follow-up action.

Messages:

Date/Time: ____

Date/Time: ____

Date/Time: ____

Secretary's name ____

★ ★ ★

Follow-up Action:

❑ **Yes, There Is an Interest:**

Build your marketing plan by gathering as much information as you can about the position. Take notes!

Position/title: ______________________________

Position reports to: ______________________________

Skills/experience required:

Interview date/time: ______________________________

Directions:

★ ★ ★

❑ **No Interest or No Position:**

Ask for a referral!

Name of referred company: ______________________________

Name/title of referred employer: ______________________________

Address: ______________________________

____

____

Telephone Number: ____________________

★ ★ ★

❑ **Has Not Seen Resume:**

Geographically local employer — Suggest that you drop off the resume at a specified date and time. If employer says yes, proceed to ❑ **Yes, There Is an Interest** and build your marketing plan and set up an appointment. If employer responds by saying no interest or nothing open, proceed to ❑ **No Interest or No Position** and ask for a referral.

Geographically distant employer — Establish most expeditious method of sending information to employer with follow-up date and time.

Follow-up date/time: ____________________

If there is no interest or position, ask for a referral.

RMF Employer Contact Form

Contact Dates:

Date mailed: ______________________________ Anticipated follow-up date ________________

Actual follow-up date ______________________

★ ★ ★ ★ ★

Research Phase:

Organization's Name: ____

Contact Name/Title: ____

Address: ____

____

Telephone Number: ___________________________ Fax Number: _________________________

Notes:

Build your cover letter based on the research you have conducted. Place your letter along with your resume in the mail and move to the Mail Phase.

★ ★ ★ ★ ★

Mail Phase:

For geographically local companies, wait 4 to 6 days and then proceed to the Follow-up Phase. For geographically distant companies wait 5 to 7 days and then proceed to the Follow-up Phase. Begin doing research on more companies.

★ ★ ★ ★ ★

Follow-up Phase:

Place telephone call to the employer.

1) Introduce yourself
2) Tell purpose of phone call
3) Present 20-second commercial
4) Determine if there is an interest
5) Go to back of contact form and follow appropriate follow-up action.

Messages:

Date/Time: ____

Date/Time: ____

Date/Time: ____

Secretary's name ____

★ ★ ★

Follow-up Action:

❑ **Yes, There Is an Interest:**

Build your marketing plan by gathering as much information as you can about the position. Take notes!

Position/title: ____________________

Position reports to: ____________________

Skills/experience required:

Interview date/time: ____________________

Directions:

★ ★ ★

❑ **No Interest or No Position:**

Ask for a referral!

Name of referred company: ____________________

Name/title of referred employer: ____________________

Address: ____________________

____

____

Telephone Number: ____________________

★ ★ ★

❑ **Has Not Seen Resume:**

Geographically local employer — Suggest that you drop off the resume at a specified date and time. If employer says yes, proceed to ❑ **Yes, There Is an Interest** and build your marketing plan and set up an appointment. If employer responds by saying no interest or nothing open, proceed to ❑ **No Interest or No Position** and ask for a referral.

Geographically distant employer — Establish most expeditious method of sending information to employer with follow-up date and time.

Follow-up date/time: ____________________

If there is no interest or position, ask for a referral.

RMF Employer Contact Form

Contact Dates:

Date mailed: ______________________ Anticipated follow-up date ______________

Actual follow-up date ______________

★ ★ ★ ★ ★

Research Phase:

Organization's Name: ______________________

Contact Name/Title: ______________________

Address: ______________________

____

Telephone Number: ______________ Fax Number: ______________

Notes:

Build your cover letter based on the research you have conducted. Place your letter along with your resume in the mail and move to the Mail Phase.

★ ★ ★ ★ ★

Mail Phase:

For geographically local companies, wait 4 to 6 days and then proceed to the Follow-up Phase.
For geographically distant companies wait 5 to 7 days and then proceed to the Follow-up Phase.
Begin doing research on more companies.

★ ★ ★ ★ ★

Follow-up Phase:

Place telephone call to the employer.

1) Introduce yourself
2) Tell purpose of phone call
3) Present 20-second commercial
4) Determine if there is an interest
5) Go to back of contact form and follow appropriate follow-up action.

Messages:

Date/Time: ______________________

Date/Time: ______________________

Date/Time: ______________________

Secretary's name ______________________

★ ★ ★

Follow-up Action:

❑ **Yes, There Is an Interest:**

Build your marketing plan by gathering as much information as you can about the position. Take notes!

Position/title: ____________________

Position reports to: ____________________

Skills/experience required:

Interview date/time: ____________________

Directions:

★ ★ ★

❑ **No Interest or No Position:**

Ask for a referral!

Name of referred company: ____________________

Name/title of referred employer: ____________________

Address: ____________________

____

____

Telephone Number: ____________________

★ ★ ★

❑ **Has Not Seen Resume:**

Geographically local employer — Suggest that you drop off the resume at a specified date and time. If employer says yes, proceed to ❑ **Yes, There Is an Interest** and build your marketing plan and set up an appointment. If employer responds by saying no interest or nothing open, proceed to ❑ **No Interest or No Position** and ask for a referral.

Geographically distant employer — Establish most expeditious method of sending information to employer with follow-up date and time.

Follow-up date/time: ____________________

If there is no interest or position, ask for a referral.

RMF Employer Contact Form

Contact Dates:
Date mailed: ______________________ Anticipated follow-up date ______________
Actual follow-up date __________________

★ ★ ★ ★ ★

Research Phase:
Organization's Name: ____
Contact Name/Title: ____
Address: ____
____
Telephone Number: ____________________ Fax Number: ____________________
Notes:

Build your cover letter based on the research you have conducted. Place your letter along with your resume in the mail and move to the Mail Phase.

★ ★ ★ ★ ★

Mail Phase:
For geographically local companies, wait 4 to 6 days and then proceed to the Follow-up Phase.
For geographically distant companies wait 5 to 7 days and then proceed to the Follow-up Phase.
Begin doing research on more companies.

★ ★ ★ ★ ★

Follow-up Phase:
Place telephone call to the employer.

1) Introduce yourself
2) Tell purpose of phone call
3) Present 20-second commercial
4) Determine if there is an interest
5) Go to back of contact form and follow appropriate follow-up action.

Messages:
Date/Time: ____
Date/Time: ____
Date/Time: ____

Secretary's name ____

★ ★ ★

Follow-up Action:

❏ **Yes, There Is an Interest:**

Build your marketing plan by gathering as much information as you can about the position. Take notes!

Position/title: ______________________________

Position reports to: ______________________________

Skills/experience required:

Interview date/time: ______________________________

Directions:

★ ★ ★

❏ **No Interest or No Position:**

Ask for a referral!

Name of referred company: ______________________________

Name/title of referred employer: ______________________________

Address: ______________________________

____

____

Telephone Number: ______________________________

★ ★ ★

❏ **Has Not Seen Resume:**

Geographically local employer — Suggest that you drop off the resume at a specified date and time. If employer says yes, proceed to ❏ **Yes, There Is an Interest** and build your marketing plan and set up an appointment. If employer responds by saying no interest or nothing open, proceed to ❏ **No Interest or No Position** and ask for a referral.

Geographically distant employer — Establish most expeditious method of sending information to employer with follow-up date and time.

Follow-up date/time: ______________________________

If there is no interest or position, ask for a referral.

RMF Employer Contact Form

Contact Dates:
Date mailed: ____________________________ Anticipated follow-up date ________________
Actual follow-up date ____________________

★ ★ ★ ★ ★

Research Phase:
Organization's Name: ____
Contact Name/Title: ____
Address: ____
____
Telephone Number: __________________________ Fax Number: _________________________
Notes:

Build your cover letter based on the research you have conducted. Place your letter along with your resume in the mail and move to the Mail Phase.

★ ★ ★ ★ ★

Mail Phase:
For geographically local companies, wait 4 to 6 days and then proceed to the Follow-up Phase.
For geographically distant companies wait 5 to 7 days and then proceed to the Follow-up Phase.
Begin doing research on more companies.

★ ★ ★ ★ ★

Follow-up Phase:
Place telephone call to the employer.

1) Introduce yourself
2) Tell purpose of phone call
3) Present 20-second commercial
4) Determine if there is an interest
5) Go to back of contact form and follow appropriate follow-up action.

Messages:
Date/Time: ____
Date/Time: ____
Date/Time: ____

Secretary's name ____

★ ★ ★

FOLLOW-UP ACTION:

❑ **Yes, There Is an Interest:**

Build your marketing plan by gathering as much information as you can about the position. Take notes!

Position/title: ______________________________

Position reports to: ______________________________

Skills/experience required:

Interview date/time: ______________________________

Directions:

★ ★ ★

❑ **No Interest or No Position:**

Ask for a referral!

Name of referred company: ______________________________

Name/title of referred employer: ______________________________

Address: ______________________________

____

____

Telephone Number: ______________________________

★ ★ ★

❑ **Has Not Seen Resume:**

Geographically local employer — Suggest that you drop off the resume at a specified date and time. If employer says yes, proceed to ❑ **Yes, There Is an Interest** and build your marketing plan and set up an appointment. If employer responds by saying no interest or nothing open, proceed to ❑ **No Interest or No Position** and ask for a referral.

Geographically distant employer — Establish most expeditious method of sending information to employer with follow-up date and time.

Follow-up date/time: ______________________________

If there is no interest or position, ask for a referral.

RMF Employer Contact Form

Contact Dates:

Date mailed: ______________________ Anticipated follow-up date ______________

Actual follow-up date ________________

★ ★ ★ ★ ★

Research Phase:

Organization's Name: ____

Contact Name/Title: ____

Address: ____

____

Telephone Number: ______________________ Fax Number: ____________________

Notes:

Build your cover letter based on the research you have conducted. Place your letter along with your resume in the mail and move to the Mail Phase.

★ ★ ★ ★ ★

Mail Phase:

For geographically local companies, wait 4 to 6 days and then proceed to the Follow-up Phase. For geographically distant companies wait 5 to 7 days and then proceed to the Follow-up Phase. Begin doing research on more companies.

★ ★ ★ ★ ★

Follow-up Phase:

Place telephone call to the employer.

1) Introduce yourself
2) Tell purpose of phone call
3) Present 20-second commercial
4) Determine if there is an interest
5) Go to back of contact form and follow appropriate follow-up action.

Messages:

Date/Time: ____

Date/Time: ____

Date/Time: ____

Secretary's name ____

★ ★ ★

Follow-up Action:

❑ **Yes, There Is an Interest:**

Build your marketing plan by gathering as much information as you can about the position. Take notes!

Position/title: ______________________________

Position reports to: ______________________________

Skills/experience required:

Interview date/time: ______________________________

Directions:

★ ★ ★

❑ **No Interest or No Position:**

Ask for a referral!

Name of referred company: ______________________________

Name/title of referred employer: ______________________________

Address: ______________________________

____

____

Telephone Number: ____________________

★ ★ ★

❑ **Has Not Seen Resume:**

Geographically local employer — Suggest that you drop off the resume at a specified date and time. If employer says yes, proceed to ❑ **Yes, There Is an Interest** and build your marketing plan and set up an appointment. If employer responds by saying no interest or nothing open, proceed to ❑ **No Interest or No Position** and ask for a referral.

Geographically distant employer — Establish most expeditious method of sending information to employer with follow-up date and time.

Follow-up date/time: ____________________

If there is no interest or position, ask for a referral.

RMF Employer Contact Form

Contact Dates:

Date mailed: ____________________ Anticipated follow-up date ____________

Actual follow-up date ____________

☆ ☆ ☆ ☆ ☆

Research Phase:

Organization's Name: ____________________

Contact Name/Title: ____________________

Address: ____________________

____

Telephone Number: ____________________ Fax Number: ____________

Notes:

Build your cover letter based on the research you have conducted. Place your letter along with your resume in the mail and move to the Mail Phase.

☆ ☆ ☆ ☆ ☆

Mail Phase:

For geographically local companies, wait 4 to 6 days and then proceed to the Follow-up Phase. For geographically distant companies wait 5 to 7 days and then proceed to the Follow-up Phase. Begin doing research on more companies.

☆ ☆ ☆ ☆ ☆

Follow-up Phase:

Place telephone call to the employer.

1) Introduce yourself
2) Tell purpose of phone call
3) Present 20-second commercial
4) Determine if there is an interest
5) Go to back of contact form and follow appropriate follow-up action.

Messages:

Date/Time: ____________________

Date/Time: ____________________

Date/Time: ____________________

Secretary's name ____________________

★ ★ ★

FOLLOW-UP ACTION:

❑ **Yes, There Is an Interest:**

Build your marketing plan by gathering as much information as you can about the position. Take notes!

Position/title: ______________________________

Position reports to: ______________________________

Skills/experience required:

Interview date/time: ______________________________

Directions:

★ ★ ★

❑ **No Interest or No Position:**

Ask for a referral!

Name of referred company: ______________________________

Name/title of referred employer: ______________________________

Address: ______________________________

____

____

Telephone Number: ____________________

★ ★ ★

❑ **Has Not Seen Resume:**

Geographically local employer — Suggest that you drop off the resume at a specified date and time. If employer says yes, proceed to ❑ **Yes, There Is an Interest** and build your marketing plan and set up an appointment. If employer responds by saying no interest or nothing open, proceed to ❑ **No Interest or No Position** and ask for a referral.

Geographically distant employer — Establish most expeditious method of sending information to employer with follow-up date and time.

Follow-up date/time: ____________________

If there is no interest or position, ask for a referral.

RMF Employer Contact Form

Contact Dates:

Date mailed: ______________________ Anticipated follow-up date ______________

Actual follow-up date ______________

★ ★ ★ ★ ★

Research Phase:

Organization's Name: ____

Contact Name/Title: ____

Address: ____

____

Telephone Number: ______________________ Fax Number: ______________________

Notes:

Build your cover letter based on the research you have conducted. Place your letter along with your resume in the mail and move to the Mail Phase.

★ ★ ★ ★ ★

Mail Phase:

For geographically local companies, wait 4 to 6 days and then proceed to the Follow-up Phase. For geographically distant companies wait 5 to 7 days and then proceed to the Follow-up Phase. Begin doing research on more companies.

★ ★ ★ ★ ★

Follow-up Phase:

Place telephone call to the employer.

1) Introduce yourself
2) Tell purpose of phone call
3) Present 20-second commercial
4) Determine if there is an interest
5) Go to back of contact form and follow appropriate follow-up action.

Messages:

Date/Time: ____

Date/Time: ____

Date/Time: ____

Secretary's name ____

★ ★ ★

Follow-up Action:

❑ **Yes, There Is an Interest:**

Build your marketing plan by gathering as much information as you can about the position. Take notes!

Position/title: ______________________________

Position reports to: ______________________________

Skills/experience required:

Interview date/time: ______________________________

Directions:

★ ★ ★

❑ **No Interest or No Position:**

Ask for a referral!

Name of referred company: ______________________________

Name/title of referred employer: ______________________________

Address: ______________________________

____

____

Telephone Number: ______________________________

★ ★ ★

❑ **Has Not Seen Resume:**

Geographically local employer — Suggest that you drop off the resume at a specified date and time. If employer says yes, proceed to ❑ **Yes, There Is an Interest** and build your marketing plan and set up an appointment. If employer responds by saying no interest or nothing open, proceed to ❑ **No Interest or No Position** and ask for a referral.

Geographically distant employer — Establish most expeditious method of sending information to employer with follow-up date and time.

Follow-up date/time: ______________________________

If there is no interest or position, ask for a referral.

RMF EMPLOYER CONTACT FORM

Contact Dates:

Date mailed: ______________________ Anticipated follow-up date ______________

Actual follow-up date __________________

☆ ☆ ☆ ☆ ☆

RESEARCH PHASE:

Organization's Name: ____

Contact Name/Title: ____

Address: ____

____

Telephone Number: ____________________ Fax Number: ____________________

Notes:

Build your cover letter based on the research you have conducted. Place your letter along with your resume in the mail and move to the Mail Phase.

☆ ☆ ☆ ☆ ☆

MAIL PHASE:

For geographically local companies, wait 4 to 6 days and then proceed to the Follow-up Phase. For geographically distant companies wait 5 to 7 days and then proceed to the Follow-up Phase. Begin doing research on more companies.

☆ ☆ ☆ ☆ ☆

FOLLOW-UP PHASE:

Place telephone call to the employer.

1) Introduce yourself
2) Tell purpose of phone call
3) Present 20-second commercial
4) Determine if there is an interest
5) Go to back of contact form and follow appropriate follow-up action.

Messages:

Date/Time: ____

Date/Time: ____

Date/Time: ____

Secretary's name ____

★ ★ ★

Follow-up Action:

❑ **Yes, There Is an Interest:**

Build your marketing plan by gathering as much information as you can about the position. Take notes!

Position/title: ____________________

Position reports to: ____________________

Skills/experience required:

Interview date/time: ____________________

Directions:

★ ★ ★

❑ **No Interest or No Position:**

Ask for a referral!

Name of referred company: ____________________

Name/title of referred employer: ____________________

Address: ____________________

____

____

Telephone Number: ____________________

★ ★ ★

❑ **Has Not Seen Resume:**

Geographically local employer — Suggest that you drop off the resume at a specified date and time. If employer says yes, proceed to ❑ **Yes, There Is an Interest** and build your marketing plan and set up an appointment. If employer responds by saying no interest or nothing open, proceed to ❑ **No Interest or No Position** and ask for a referral.

Geographically distant employer — Establish most expeditious method of sending information to employer with follow-up date and time.

Follow-up date/time: ____________________

If there is no interest or position, ask for a referral.

RMF Employer Contact Form

Contact Dates:

Date mailed: ______________________ Anticipated follow-up date ______________

Actual follow-up date ________________

★ ★ ★ ★ ★

Research Phase:

Organization's Name: ____

Contact Name/Title: ____

Address: ____

____

Telephone Number: ____________________ Fax Number: ____________________

Notes:

Build your cover letter based on the research you have conducted. Place your letter along with your resume in the mail and move to the Mail Phase.

★ ★ ★ ★ ★

Mail Phase:

For geographically local companies, wait 4 to 6 days and then proceed to the Follow-up Phase. For geographically distant companies wait 5 to 7 days and then proceed to the Follow-up Phase. Begin doing research on more companies.

★ ★ ★ ★ ★

Follow-up Phase:

Place telephone call to the employer.

1) Introduce yourself
2) Tell purpose of phone call
3) Present 20-second commercial
4) Determine if there is an interest
5) Go to back of contact form and follow appropriate follow-up action.

Messages:

Date/Time: ____

Date/Time: ____

Date/Time: ____

Secretary's name ____

★ ★ ★

FOLLOW-UP ACTION:

❑ **Yes, There Is an Interest:**

Build your marketing plan by gathering as much information as you can about the position. Take notes!

Position/title: ______________________________

Position reports to: ______________________________

Skills/experience required:

Interview date/time: ______________________________

Directions:

★ ★ ★

❑ **No Interest or No Position:**

Ask for a referral!

Name of referred company: ______________________________

Name/title of referred employer: ______________________________

Address: ______________________________

____

____

Telephone Number: ____________________

★ ★ ★

❑ **Has Not Seen Resume:**

Geographically local employer — Suggest that you drop off the resume at a specified date and time. If employer says yes, proceed to ❑ **Yes, There Is an Interest** and build your marketing plan and set up an appointment. If employer responds by saying no interest or nothing open, proceed to ❑ **No Interest or No Position** and ask for a referral.

Geographically distant employer — Establish most expeditious method of sending information to employer with follow-up date and time.

Follow-up date/time: ____________________

If there is no interest or position, ask for a referral.

RMF Employer Contact Form

Contact Dates:
Date mailed: ____________________ Anticipated follow-up date ____________
Actual follow-up date ______________

☆ ☆ ☆ ☆ ☆

Research Phase:
Organization's Name: ______________________________
Contact Name/Title: ______________________________
Address: ______________________________

____

Telephone Number: ____________________ Fax Number: ______________
Notes:

Build your cover letter based on the research you have conducted. Place your letter along with your resume in the mail and move to the Mail Phase.

☆ ☆ ☆ ☆ ☆

Mail Phase:
For geographically local companies, wait 4 to 6 days and then proceed to the Follow-up Phase.
For geographically distant companies wait 5 to 7 days and then proceed to the Follow-up Phase.
Begin doing research on more companies.

☆ ☆ ☆ ☆ ☆

Follow-up Phase:
Place telephone call to the employer.

1) Introduce yourself
2) Tell purpose of phone call
3) Present 20-second commercial
4) Determine if there is an interest
5) Go to back of contact form and follow appropriate follow-up action.

Messages:
Date/Time: ______________________________
Date/Time: ______________________________
Date/Time: ______________________________

Secretary's name ______________________________

★ ★ ★

FOLLOW-UP ACTION:

❑ **Yes, There Is an Interest:**

Build your marketing plan by gathering as much information as you can about the position. Take notes!

Position/title: ______________________________

Position reports to: ______________________________

Skills/experience required:

Interview date/time: ______________________________

Directions:

★ ★ ★

❑ **No Interest or No Position:**

Ask for a referral!

Name of referred company: ______________________________

Name/title of referred employer: ______________________________

Address: ______________________________

____

____

Telephone Number: ____________________

★ ★ ★

❑ **Has Not Seen Resume:**

Geographically local employer — Suggest that you drop off the resume at a specified date and time. If employer says yes, proceed to ❑ **Yes, There Is an Interest** and build your marketing plan and set up an appointment. If employer responds by saying no interest or nothing open, proceed to ❑ **No Interest or No Position** and ask for a referral.

Geographically distant employer — Establish most expeditious method of sending information to employer with follow-up date and time.

Follow-up date/time: ____________________

If there is no interest or position, ask for a referral.

RMF Employer Contact Form

Contact Dates:

Date mailed: ______________________ Anticipated follow-up date ______________

Actual follow-up date ______________

★ ★ ★ ★ ★

Research Phase:

Organization's Name: ______________________________________

Contact Name/Title: ______________________________________

Address: ______________________________________

____

Telephone Number: ______________________ Fax Number: ______________________

Notes:

Build your cover letter based on the research you have conducted. Place your letter along with your resume in the mail and move to the Mail Phase.

★ ★ ★ ★ ★

Mail Phase:

For geographically local companies, wait 4 to 6 days and then proceed to the Follow-up Phase. For geographically distant companies wait 5 to 7 days and then proceed to the Follow-up Phase. Begin doing research on more companies.

★ ★ ★ ★ ★

Follow-up Phase:

Place telephone call to the employer.

1) Introduce yourself
2) Tell purpose of phone call
3) Present 20-second commercial
4) Determine if there is an interest
5) Go to back of contact form and follow appropriate follow-up action.

Messages:

Date/Time: ______________________________________

Date/Time: ______________________________________

Date/Time: ______________________________________

Secretary's name ______________________________________

★ ★ ★

FOLLOW-UP ACTION:

❑ **Yes, There Is an Interest:**

Build your marketing plan by gathering as much information as you can about the position. Take notes!

Position/title: ______________________________

Position reports to: ______________________________

Skills/experience required:

Interview date/time: ______________________________

Directions:

★ ★ ★

❑ **No Interest or No Position:**

Ask for a referral!

Name of referred company: ______________________________

Name/title of referred employer: ______________________________

Address: ______________________________

____

____

Telephone Number: ____________________

★ ★ ★

❑ **Has Not Seen Resume:**

Geographically local employer — Suggest that you drop off the resume at a specified date and time. If employer says yes, proceed to ❑ **Yes, There Is an Interest** and build your marketing plan and set up an appointment. If employer responds by saying no interest or nothing open, proceed to ❑ **No Interest or No Position** and ask for a referral.

Geographically distant employer — Establish most expeditious method of sending information to employer with follow-up date and time.

Follow-up date/time: ____________________

If there is no interest or position, ask for a referral.

RMF Employer Contact Form

Contact Dates:
Date mailed: ______________________ Anticipated follow-up date ____________
Actual follow-up date ________________

★ ★ ★ ★ ★

Research Phase:
Organization's Name: ______________________________________
Contact Name/Title: ______________________________________
Address: ______________________________________
____
Telephone Number: ____________________ Fax Number: ____________________
Notes:

Build your cover letter based on the research you have conducted. Place your letter along with your resume in the mail and move to the Mail Phase.

★ ★ ★ ★ ★

Mail Phase:
For geographically local companies, wait 4 to 6 days and then proceed to the Follow-up Phase.
For geographically distant companies wait 5 to 7 days and then proceed to the Follow-up Phase.
Begin doing research on more companies.

★ ★ ★ ★ ★

Follow-up Phase:
Place telephone call to the employer.

1) Introduce yourself
2) Tell purpose of phone call
3) Present 20-second commercial
4) Determine if there is an interest
5) Go to back of contact form and follow appropriate follow-up action.

Messages:
Date/Time: ______________________________________
Date/Time: ______________________________________
Date/Time: ______________________________________

Secretary's name ______________________________________

★ ★ ★

FOLLOW-UP ACTION:

❑ **Yes, There Is an Interest:**

Build your marketing plan by gathering as much information as you can about the position. Take notes!

Position/title: ________________________________

Position reports to: ________________________________

Skills/experience required:

Interview date/time: ________________________________

Directions:

★ ★ ★

❑ **No Interest or No Position:**

Ask for a referral!

Name of referred company: ________________________________

Name/title of referred employer: ________________________________

Address: ________________________________

____

____

Telephone Number: ____________________

★ ★ ★

❑ **Has Not Seen Resume:**

Geographically local employer — Suggest that you drop off the resume at a specified date and time. If employer says yes, proceed to ❑ **Yes, There Is an Interest** and build your marketing plan and set up an appointment. If employer responds by saying no interest or nothing open, proceed to ❑ **No Interest or No Position** and ask for a referral.

Geographically distant employer — Establish most expeditious method of sending information to employer with follow-up date and time.

Follow-up date/time: ____________________

If there is no interest or position, ask for a referral.

RMF Employer Contact Form

Contact Dates:

Date mailed: ______________________ Anticipated follow-up date ______________

Actual follow-up date ______________

★ ★ ★ ★ ★

Research Phase:

Organization's Name: ______________________________________

Contact Name/Title: ______________________________________

Address: ______________________________________

____

Telephone Number: ______________________ Fax Number: ______________________

Notes:

Build your cover letter based on the research you have conducted. Place your letter along with your resume in the mail and move to the Mail Phase.

★ ★ ★ ★ ★

Mail Phase:

For geographically local companies, wait 4 to 6 days and then proceed to the Follow-up Phase. For geographically distant companies wait 5 to 7 days and then proceed to the Follow-up Phase. Begin doing research on more companies.

★ ★ ★ ★ ★

Follow-up Phase:

Place telephone call to the employer.

1) Introduce yourself
2) Tell purpose of phone call
3) Present 20-second commercial
4) Determine if there is an interest
5) Go to back of contact form and follow appropriate follow-up action.

Messages:

Date/Time: ______________________________________

Date/Time: ______________________________________

Date/Time: ______________________________________

Secretary's name ______________________________________

★ ★ ★

FOLLOW-UP ACTION:

❑ **Yes, There Is an Interest:**

Build your marketing plan by gathering as much information as you can about the position. Take notes!

Position/title: ______________________________

Position reports to: ______________________________

Skills/experience required:

Interview date/time: ______________________________

Directions:

★ ★ ★

❑ **No Interest or No Position:**

Ask for a referral!

Name of referred company: ______________________________

Name/title of referred employer: ______________________________

Address: ______________________________
____
____

Telephone Number: ______________________________

★ ★ ★

❑ **Has Not Seen Resume:**

Geographically local employer — Suggest that you drop off the resume at a specified date and time. If employer says yes, proceed to ❑ **Yes, There Is an Interest** and build your marketing plan and set up an appointment. If employer responds by saying no interest or nothing open, proceed to ❑ **No Interest or No Position** and ask for a referral.

Geographically distant employer — Establish most expeditious method of sending information to employer with follow-up date and time.

Follow-up date/time: ______________________________

If there is no interest or position, ask for a referral.

RMF Employer Contact Form

Contact Dates:
Date mailed: ______________________ Anticipated follow-up date ______________
Actual follow-up date ______________

★ ★ ★ ★ ★

Research Phase:
Organization's Name: ______________________________
Contact Name/Title: ______________________________
Address: ______________________________
____
Telephone Number: ______________ Fax Number: ______________
Notes:

Build your cover letter based on the research you have conducted. Place your letter along with your resume in the mail and move to the Mail Phase.

★ ★ ★ ★ ★

Mail Phase:
For geographically local companies, wait 4 to 6 days and then proceed to the Follow-up Phase.
For geographically distant companies wait 5 to 7 days and then proceed to the Follow-up Phase.
Begin doing research on more companies.

★ ★ ★ ★ ★

Follow-up Phase:
Place telephone call to the employer.

1) Introduce yourself
2) Tell purpose of phone call
3) Present 20-second commercial
4) Determine if there is an interest
5) Go to back of contact form and follow appropriate follow-up action.

Messages:
Date/Time: ______________________________
Date/Time: ______________________________
Date/Time: ______________________________

Secretary's name ______________________________

★ ★ ★

FOLLOW-UP ACTION:

❑ **Yes, There Is an Interest:**

Build your marketing plan by gathering as much information as you can about the position. Take notes!

Position/title: ______________________________

Position reports to: ______________________________

Skills/experience required:

Interview date/time: ______________________________

Directions:

★ ★ ★

❑ **No Interest or No Position:**

Ask for a referral!

Name of referred company: ______________________________

Name/title of referred employer: ______________________________

Address: ______________________________

____

____

Telephone Number: ____________________

★ ★ ★

❑ **Has Not Seen Resume:**

Geographically local employer — Suggest that you drop off the resume at a specified date and time. If employer says yes, proceed to ❑ **Yes, There Is an Interest** and build your marketing plan and set up an appointment. If employer responds by saying no interest or nothing open, proceed to ❑ **No Interest or No Position** and ask for a referral.

Geographically distant employer — Establish most expeditious method of sending information to employer with follow-up date and time.

Follow-up date/time: ____________________

If there is no interest or position, ask for a referral.

RMF Employer Contact Form

Contact Dates:

Date mailed: ______________________________ Anticipated follow-up date ______________

Actual follow-up date ______________

★ ★ ★ ★ ★

Research Phase:

Organization's Name: ____

Contact Name/Title: ____

Address: ____

____

Telephone Number: ______________________ Fax Number: ______________________

Notes:

Build your cover letter based on the research you have conducted. Place your letter along with your resume in the mail and move to the Mail Phase.

★ ★ ★ ★ ★

Mail Phase:

For geographically local companies, wait 4 to 6 days and then proceed to the Follow-up Phase. For geographically distant companies wait 5 to 7 days and then proceed to the Follow-up Phase. Begin doing research on more companies.

★ ★ ★ ★ ★

Follow-up Phase:

Place telephone call to the employer.

1) Introduce yourself
2) Tell purpose of phone call
3) Present 20-second commercial
4) Determine if there is an interest
5) Go to back of contact form and follow appropriate follow-up action.

Messages:

Date/Time: ____

Date/Time: ____

Date/Time: ____

Secretary's name ____

★ ★ ★

FOLLOW-UP ACTION:

❑ **Yes, There Is an Interest:**

Build your marketing plan by gathering as much information as you can about the position. Take notes!

Position/title: ______________________________

Position reports to: ______________________________

Skills/experience required:

Interview date/time: ______________________________

Directions:

★ ★ ★

❑ **No Interest or No Position:**

Ask for a referral!

Name of referred company: ______________________________

Name/title of referred employer: ______________________________

Address: ______________________________

____

____

Telephone Number: ____________________

★ ★ ★

❑ **Has Not Seen Resume:**

Geographically local employer — Suggest that you drop off the resume at a specified date and time. If employer says yes, proceed to ❑ **Yes, There Is an Interest** and build your marketing plan and set up an appointment. If employer responds by saying no interest or nothing open, proceed to ❑ **No Interest or No Position** and ask for a referral.

Geographically distant employer — Establish most expeditious method of sending information to employer with follow-up date and time.

Follow-up date/time: ____________________

If there is no interest or position, ask for a referral.